The Management of Angling Waters

Alex Behrendt

Sketches by Katharine Behrendt

ANDRE DEUTSCH

First published 1977 by
André Deutsch Limited
105 Great Russell Street London WC1

Printed in Great Britain by
Ebenezer Baylis & Son Limited
The Trinity Press Worcester and London

ISBN 0 233 96857 1

Contents

List of Plates 7

1 Curtain Raiser 9
The Site
Water Supply
Security of Tenure

2 Preparing the Site 20
The Monk

3 Building a Lake Fishery 36

4 The Rules 60

5 River Management 95
Financial Matters
Altering a Stream and Making it Fishable
Weed
Mud
Stocking
Hatcheries and Stewponds in a Fishery
Vermin

6 Management of a Small Trout Lake Fishery 122
Weed
Mud
Stocking
Keeping the Lake in Good Trim

7 Management of Coarse Fish Fisheries 143
Pike
Trout, Chub and Eel
Perch and Zander
Carp and Bream
Roach, Rudd and Crucian Carp

Tench
Stocking, Close Season, Size Limit

8 The Underwater Food Animals 175
Plankton and Midges
Day-flies and Sedges
Water Hog Louse and Shrimp
Snails
Crayfish
Minnow and Stickleback

9 Publicity for Fisheries 194

Index 203

List of Plates

Facing page

The level of the water in the lake is slowly rising 32
The end of the outflow pipe

Giving the dam the correct angle 33
The final job for the bulldozer

A collapsed dam 64
When cracks appear a dam must be rebuilt

An overflow under construction 65
The elver trap

A simple shelter 96
All dams must be wide enough to carry a road
Lintels make excellent bridges

Alsatians are a must for well keepered waters 97
A wheelbarrow for work around the fishery

Weed cutting 128
Clearing rubbish

Building a stewpond 129
The same scene a few years later

A wooden raft for pulling weed 160
Killing weed with a polythene sheet

The first stage of netting 161
The final stage of the pull

How a pier is constructed 192
The pier when the water is at its normal level

Sexing tench 193
Aspiring fishery managers should be given the dirty jobs!

1 Curtain Raiser

Before the turn of the century, and even up to the mid 1920s, fishermen lived in a kind of Utopia. There was no pressure on fishing space, and in general there was an ample supply of wild fish to keep their creels full. Complacently, they harvested where they had never sown, and concentrated their interest on the correct ritual for catching their fish, rather than on whether or not they would always have fish to catch.

But soon, with the rapid increase of population and the proportional increase of fishermen, angling was not what it had been in the good old days. Increasing industrialization, and the resulting loss of many rivers through pollution, awakened anglers to the fact that they would have to look around for their fishing. Slowly it dawned on fishing clubs and private fisheries that the honeymoon was over, and Nature would no longer provide bountifully for their sport. For the first time, the phrase 'fishery management' began to figure in fishing conversation.

Some far-sighted people started work on the improvement of angling waters; both rivers and lakes. Of course, these people did not have an easy time of it. They had no extensive literature to refer to and no precedents to follow. Everything had to be discovered by trial and error. Some books, however, were published even then and reading them now, many years later, we should not be too patronizing about their misconceptions: we have come a long way and have learnt a lot. In the past few years especially, many problems have been solved and mysteries explained. But there is still a great deal to be learned.

Fish farmers were in a more fortunate position, because they had about a thousand years of history behind them. They had produced fish for food as a profession, but angling as a hobby has no history of management. Perhaps it was a mistake that in the early years of fishery management the cooperation and advice of the fish farmers was not sought. A few fish farmers gave advice to clubs and private owners, but unfortunately the clubs and owners mostly preferred to have a fisherman take over the management. An angler almost always approaches management problems only from the catching aspect. He does not recognise that fishery management is something else entirely: it is the years it took to bring the fish to a catchable size and the creating of a suitable water in which to catch it, that really matters. As most anglers tend to be bored by this approach it follows that the people responsible for the management of angling waters – and this applies especially to clubs – must be of a particular type. If they are fanatical anglers, most probably they will be bad fishery managers. In a lifetime spent in fisheries or in fishery management, I have found that such men can never shake off an amateur approach. The best managers I know are non-anglers. Of course, they know everything there is to know about how to catch fish and about tackle but the actual catching doesn't excite them. I always say if you are a publican, you should leave the liquor alone!

Right from the beginning, I cannot stress strongly enough the importance of proper training for fishery management. The policies of an angling club are decided, in most instances, by a committee. But if the fishery manager of a club water has a proper knowledge of his job, the committee will accept his suggestions. For example, how can the members know what fish are most suitable for their particular water? They may wish to introduce species of fish other than those already there. It is then up to the manager to explain that water is like land: on some soils you can grow certain crops successfully, while other crops do badly or fail completely. Land covered with water is the same. No two lakes or rivers are exactly alike but as anglers often prefer some species of fish to others, they are often determined to stock with the fish of their choice, irrespective of whether or not the water is suitable. In these circumstances the glass-case monster of the angler's dreams will never grow to a glass-case size, and the only fish caught will be run-of-the-mill tiddlers: old in years, but small in size.

When a new trend develops, such as the recent interest in fishery management and the creation of new fisheries, there is sure to be a bumper crop of experts. They crawl out of the woodwork and from under stones – people who have no knowledge of, or interest in, the real objectives, but who join the movement only for what they can get out of it. Again and again I am astonished at meeting managers who have not managed, but *mis*managed their particular stretch of river or lake. When questioned, they reveal that they have been advised by 'experts' – self-styled experts whose chief expertise is their ability to obtain remarkably high fees. However, it is possible to protect yourself against these characters. In any other business you would ask for references – so why not do the same in this instance? You must ask whether the applicant is in charge of a fishery, and whether it is successful. Has it been successful for a long time? How many fisheries has he created? Are they flourishing? If the success score is high, the expert has much to offer. But if there is no score, then you can start a discussion about ethics.

There are a number of fisheries which are run successfully by men and by women too. These fisheries have weathered many ups and downs of fortune, and can serve as models. They provide good sport and their finances are healthy. The men and women who run them have the knowledge, good sense and the will to work, which add up to a recipe for success. They do not possess a bottle of magic potion which, if added (a drop every morning and two drops every evening) to their waters, will work miracles.

The trout fishing clubs have frequently sought advice from trout farmers. But, so far as I know, coarse fish angling clubs have never asked advice from a coarse fish farmer. Of late, study groups have been formed amongst anglers to research into the life history of carp, tench, and many other coarse fish. I have met some of these groups, and when they told me what they wanted to know, I could only tell them that any coarse fish farmer worth his salt deals with these matters every day of his life and knows the answers. Of course, it does no harm if anglers play at being researchers. It may increase their knowledge. But if there are fees involved, money that could be put to good use in the fisheries might be wasted.

It is as well not to confine yourself in the search for information and advice. In the next valley, and the valley beyond that, and one valley further still, there is a lot of activity, and by using your initiative you can get your hands on publications not only from every nearby valley, but from all over the world. For instance, in the United States a tremendous amount of work has been done, and experience gained, in the running of trout fisheries. In Poland, Czechoslovakia, Hungary and Russia, much experience is being gained in the management of coarse fishing waters. These last mentioned countries have taken things even a step further and combine recreational fishing with food production: they stock put and take coarse fisheries, and the fisherman takes home his catch for the family supper. With the rapid increase in population and the need for food, this is a far-sighted policy. Already, we in England, take home and eat the salmon and trout we have caught. I see the day coming when coarse fishing will have the same double objective.

But there are still other aspects of the sport of fishing, aside from recreation (so much more important now, with the shorter working week and consequent increase of leisure time), and the possibility of obtaining a good, square meal. There are factors of economic importance. Fisheries are often created on land which is useless for agriculture or sylviculture. For example, gravel pits, useless except as rubbish dumps, make very good fisheries. Then there is the tackle industry which turns over a vast amount of money: it supplies the special clothing and gadgets considered necessary by the fishermen. In some areas the hotel industry is largely dependent on fishing and then there are too the fishing writers and fishing publications. Fishing also provides a lifetime's employment for keepers and ghillies who will all do better as the sport increases. It is to the advantage of all that the existing fisheries are efficiently run, and that new fisheries are built as economically and as efficiently as possible.

In any discussion about the management of angling waters, strict rules should not be laid down. As I have said, no two rivers and no two lakes are alike. Even when lakes are a few metres apart, they differ. Fishery management has some precepts which are basic, but otherwise management must be flexible and adjusted to local conditions. Angling waters fall into three classes: the first is the rod-letting fishery run by an estate or by a private individual who has the fishery as his main occupation. The second is the fishery which is run only for the owner himself and his friends, and this may be a small syndicate with no profit motive. The third is the angling club. The management of these types of fisheries will be discussed at length in a later chapter. The points that will be covered apply equally to the re-establishment of a stream or river fishery which has fallen into disuse, as to a stream or river never before used as a fishery. But, to begin at the beginning, we should rightly consider the creation of a lake fishery from scratch.

The Site

If you are proposing to create a lake fishery you must first do some market research. This does not apply to people wishing to form a club, because such a group will probably seek a fishery as close as possible to their homes. Nor does it apply to anglers forming a syndicate who have only themselves to please and can probably go further afield, especially if they are young men and don't mind driving long distances. But a man who wants to create a fishery and make it his livelihood, be it game or coarse fishing, has to think very carefully indeed about the location. Most of the people running fisheries as businesses at present, however, didn't locate their fisheries in this way. They simply found a stretch of water and bought it. Thus, if the water was in a good area, where there was a demand for fishing, and if it was properly managed, the fishery was a success. But if the area was wrong, perhaps too remote, or with too many other fisheries near by, the result was failure. Often there was financial loss, and bitter disappointment. Although this has happened in Europe and in North America it has not happened yet in Britain. But there has been a recent serious outbreak of the lake building disease here – people digging expensive holes in the ground, filling them with fish, and then sitting back and waiting for the money tree to blossom. Most of these projects will join the sad parade of North American and Continental failures.

Up until the 1940s and perhaps even into the 1950s, it was held that in order to be successful, a fishery had to be near a heavily populated area. But in the 1960s many anglers became car owners and distance became less of a consideration. If an angling water has a good reputation, it can be a hundred miles from the angler's home, but he will still visit it regularly and happily. This is particularly true of trout fishermen. And as for famous carp waters, where there is the attraction of thirty or forty pounders, anglers are heedless of distance and sleepless nights. Now, in the 1970s, the fisherman's wheels are not such an advantage, because of the spiralling cost of petrol and because of traffic congestion. Nevertheless, he will devise ways of overcoming the difficulties, for he has been conditioned to having to travel a certain distance to his fishing.

So, if your aim is to produce a top flight fishery, whether game or coarse fishing, you need not be concerned about your fishery being in an isolated area. But if you are going to be satisfied with an average fishery, producing reasonable sport, you would be wise to choose a site as near as possible to your potential customers.

Keep in mind the following points: try not to be too close to an existing fishery, by which I mean try not to start a game fishery near another game fishery, or a coarse fish fishery near another coarse fish fishery (of course, you can site a game fishery near a coarse fish fishery, and vice versa); try not to be bang slap on a main road with heavy traffic; try to have reasonable access; try not to be too near a housing estate or industrial development; try not to have one of your boundaries a road or a right of way; and never buy a site with a right of way through it.

Once you have decided on the area in which you wish to have your fishery, you need to find a suitable site. The first choice, obviously, is a little valley though a disused gravel pit also offers great possibilities. It is even quite possible to use a flat area which is in the water table. Invest your money in a map of the area and note all possibilities. Don't be put off by the smallness of the stream, if there is one, because you are not trying to establish a fish farm, which needs vast quantities of water (especially a trout farm), but a fishery.

There is another thing which is pertinent to the area and the site you choose. If you are proposing to have a trout fishery, you may be influenced by the number of people who prefer fishing in rivers to fishing in lakes. I have met countless trout fishermen from many parts of the world, and in my view American and Scandinavian anglers like to fish both rivers and lakes equally. British trout fishermen traditionally prefer river fishing. Only latterly, with more reservoirs being stocked with trout, and with more small lake fisheries being created, is the British angler beginning to accept still-water fishing. In Britain, it is the older generation which is complaining bitterly about the decline of river fishing, while the younger generation is quite happy with still-water fishing.

As an example of how different people judge the location of a fishery, I can best tell of the development of Two Lakes, which involves the questions of area and site and the river/still-water debate.

In 1948, when I bought two small lakes in some woodland, right between two famous chalk streams, the Test and the Itchen, and artlessly publicized the fact that I proposed to start a still-water fishery, I was told by everybody that it couldn't be done. The sporting press, when I approached them, gently enquired what fisherman in his right mind would wish to fish small lakes when the world's most famous chalk streams were so close. At that time there were no still-water fisheries in the area, and in fact there were precious few in the whole country, so there were no brains for me to pick on the subject. We had nothing to lose by trying, and my reasoning was that the Test and the Itchen already had their quota of anglers. Even though the rivers were now stocked artificially, the number of anglers could not be increased to any great extent without fundamentally altering the whole pattern of chalk stream fishing. I asked myself where all the new anglers could be accommodated. The population was increasing fast and a proportion of that population would always be anglers. Where would they fish? It was reasonable to assume that these people, not by choice, but through force of circumstances, would either take up lake fishing or have nothing at all. They might even begin to like it. I am very grateful that I was proven right. In the early years of running Two Lakes, I often heard such remarks as: 'Oh, I wish I could find some good river fishing!' or 'Now, if I had caught that fish in a river it would be perfect.' Not very kind and far from tactful. But if you run a fishery you have to develop the hide of a rhinoceros. Happily such remarks are a thing of the past. There are even a good number of people fishing Two Lakes who have a fishing ticket on a nearby river as well. If they fish the river, they enjoy that day to the full. And if they fish my lakes, they enjoy that day, too, to the full.

Water Supply

Before you commit yourself to buying a site for your lake, investigate the water supply very carefully indeed. If the site is near a river from which you can divert water, or in the water table of a river, or if there is a stream running through the site, you are well away, so long as the running water, river or stream, is not polluted. So long, too, as the river or stream can support fish. Scoop around in the shallows with a little plankton net and see what you can find. If there are shrimps in your catch you can be sure that there is no significant pollution; likewise if there are nymphs of the day flies. Have the water analysed, to check on what the shrimps and nymphs have told you about pollution, and to determine the pH value and the degree of oxygenation.

Be very suspicious of any pumping activities upstream. Obtain official facts about the amount of water being abstracted, and about the possibility of increased abstraction in the future. Make notes of the water flow, both in summer and winter.

If you are considering a disused gravel pit, do the same thing. Scoop around as far as you can with a small plankton net to find out what sort of creatures are in residence and have the water analysed. Again, be alert to any pumping activities in the vicinity. With a site where the water table is high, beware of pumping activities *below* the site. The powers-that-be show a lively interest in water abstraction above the site of a lake, but they appear to be unaware of how damaging abstraction can be below, or, so to speak, downstream from the site. When water is pumped close by from a level lower than the bottom of the lake, the water is taken from the water table, and the lake will lose water to compensate for what has been pumped away.

Take pains to make a record of all the information you collect.

There is an assumption that unless a trout lake has fresh water running through it the trout will not thrive. This is not so. If a lake is sufficiently deep in part but also has shallow areas with water plants, and does not overheat in the summer, it will support trout all the year around. It need not have the tiniest trickle of water running into it. These are lakes depending on the water table, and they must be deep so that they can stand losing a certain amount of water during a hot summer. Some people hold that even in the water table there is a certain flow which goes right through the lake or a gravel pit and so creates a current, just enough current to make the existence of trout possible. This assertion carries things a bit too far. If this infinitesimal movement qualifies as a current, then the trout must be a hypersensitive fish. Furthermore, I know of several plastic-lined ponds where no water can seep either in or out, and trout do well in them. If you wish to join in the controversy about currents and running water and how trout are effected, you will have some entertainment, and you will find many hairs to split, but don't let it influence your requirements for your lake. It's nice to have some water running into your lake, but not essential.

The inflow can be very small indeed, only sufficient to counteract evaporation and seepage. At Two Lakes it is meagre. Often when people see our inflow they can't believe that is all there is and insist that I must have hidden springs. They assume that I am keeping these a deep secret because they are part of the recipe for success, the other part being the one drop in the morning and two drops in the evening of magic potion. The inflow dries up in the summer, but the lakes are deep and I have found that the water temperature on the surface doesn't often go above 20°C when the weather is hot. If for a few days the temperature climbs another few degrees it doesn't matter, so long as the heat-wave isn't prolonged.

The water supply for coarse fish fishing lakes can be even less reliable. Most coarse fish prefer warmer water, so the lake need not be so deep. If the water temperature rises above 20°C there need be no alarm, in fact the fish will like it. You can afford to lose more water through evaporation in hot weather than you would dare to lose in a trout lake. At the risk of insulting everybody's intelligence, I must point out that a lake should not be so shallow that it dries out completely in exceptionally dry weather.

Moreover, in parts of the country where winters are severe, and lakes are covered with a thick layer of ice, all fish need deep water. Shallow lakes under thick ice can lose their entire fish population.

As a guideline, you can say that a lake three metres deep could lose one metre in a dry summer, and the trout would most likely survive in the remaining two metres. In coarse fishing waters, if the water remaining, after loss through evaporation or seepage, is only one metre, the fish will survive. In both instances I must add the proviso that before the cold weather sets in, the lake must have regained the two metres or so of depth that it had lost.

While we are on the subject of loss of water in a lake, you must remember that a newly constructed lake in its first year, and even sometimes in its second and third year, will lose a considerable amount of water through seepage. Depending on the nature of the soil below the lake, in average circumstances it takes two years for that soil to become saturated. After this the lake itself will not lose much water through seepage. Any further significant losses are caused predominantly by evaporation in very hot weather.

Security of Tenure

Some people enjoy taking up a challenge; some people enjoy a gamble, pure and simple, but there are also those innocent optimists who wander into ventures and have no realization of the booby traps neatly planted in their paths. But when the challenge proves too great, the gamble fails to pay off, the booby traps are sprung, there is a mighty bleating of shorn sheep who complain that Fate has stripped them of their all. So, in creating a fishery, as in all fields of endeavour, every step must be taken methodically and professionally. Never forget that the best time for making expensive mistakes is *before* you embark on an enterprise.

Assuming that you have found your site and made sure that the water supply is satisfactory, you can still come to grief if you have not made certain that planning permission is possible. If there is serious doubt on this point don't deceive yourself that you will be able to wangle permission by pestering the authorities, or complaining to the Minister, or having enquiries held. 'I always get what I want' is a very dangerous motto. So make sure that planning permission is possible. Go and ask.

It is not quite so easy to 'go and ask' when the questions are: will there be an aerodrome (for example) in the vicinity, or is there a possibility that there will be a motorway or road alterations which will effect you. You should visit the Roads and Bridges Department for your area and, with the greatest diplomacy, manage to get a look at maps and plans for the near and distant future.

As the years go by it will become more and more difficult to find a site for a lake or lakes, and if one is found it may not be for sale. In such circumstances it may be possible to reach an understanding with the owner, even if this should be a compromise. If the owner is a farmer for instance, he may be interested in using the water for irrigation. A legal agreement can be drawn up by which the farmer is allowed to take a certain quantity of water from the lake. However, to start a fishery under such conditions is to start at a great disadvantage. To get the best out of your fishery it must be run for a single purpose. It cannot be shared satisfactorily with irrigation, or sailing, or birdwatching, or canoeing or picnicking families.

Sooner or later then you will have to make up your mind and decide on a particular site. Perfect sites are rare, so you should accept the fact that there will always be something which could be better.

2 Preparing the Site

The first step in the building of a lake, is to fulfil the legal requirements by obtaining the permissions which are necessary. These alter each year, and are embellished annually with more and more red tape. No book can be up to date, because the situation changes so rapidly. So, at the very outset, consult the Water Authority and the Planning Authorities. They will advise you about the necessary permits.

Now you will have to provide plans for your lake and you will find that you can plan the contours with a surprising degree of accuracy. Your starting point will be where the feeder stream enters your own land from your upstream neighbour's land; this is the point above which you must not allow a backflow from your lake to creep. The backflow depends on the height of the overflow in your dam: the higher the overflow in the dam, the further back the water creeps when the lake is full. If you are not careful, the rising water will cover not only your land but also your neighbour's, and lead to a lot of trouble. It is a wise precaution to site your backflow limit a little below your starting point. Then you will make allowance for flood conditions, and you will avoid future squabbles.

From the location of your backflow limit, you can determine all levels for your lake, and a post should be driven into the ground as a mark. The top of the post must be flush with the stream, and looking downstream to where the dam will be, you mark two points corresponding with the top of the post, on each side of the valley. From these established points you can mark many more. The more marks you have, the easier it will be for the machines to work.

From these first points you can determine the height of your dam; its dimensions will depend upon the amount of water it has to hold back.

Whenever possible you should avoid having a stream run into a lake, particularly if it is a stream with a constant flow. If the land permits, and the cost can be justified, a new stream bed should be dug around the site for the lake. A sluice must be installed between the stream and the lake, and only as much water as is needed to fill the lake should be taken from the stream. Once you have your lake you will aim to take only enough to keep the lake topped up and to replace losses through seepage and evaporation.

A stream running through lakes brings a quantity of material with it, and it is amazing how much silt is deposited where the stream flows in. Silt traps can be installed, but they are cumbersome and costly to maintain. The cost of digging a new stream bed around the lake, a capital outlay which can be spread over years, is probably less in the end. With this controlled flow, worries about inadequate overflow, silting, the entry of undesired species of fish, inefficient and slow emptying of the lake, are all alleviated.

At Two Lakes unfortunately the little stream cannot be led around the lakes. The contour of the land does not permit it. In flood conditions, this little stream brings in a quantity of silt, and over three or four years the silt builds up to a metre or more around the inflow, and has to be removed at considerable cost.

When you have completed these preliminaries, you can embark on preparations for the dam itself and one of the first things you need to know is that no dam should be built across a valley on top of the existing trees, shrubs, reeds and grass. If this is done, after a year or so, the rotting vegetation will act as a drainage system under the dam. In dry seasons the lake might lose more water than the inflowing stream or the springs can replace. If this seepage were to become serious, it could even effect the safety of the dam. Therefore, the first job is to take all the top soil, including the turf, shrubs and trees, in fact *all* vegetation, clean away from the site on which the dam will 'sit'. Next, a ditch of at least half a metre deep must be dug across the valley on the dam site *after* the vegetation has been removed. This anchors the dam on the site. Figure 1 demonstrates one method, and Figure 2 an even more efficient arrangement. This tooth, or rather set of teeth descending from the dam into the foundation soil prevents most of the seepage and makes the dam safer. To

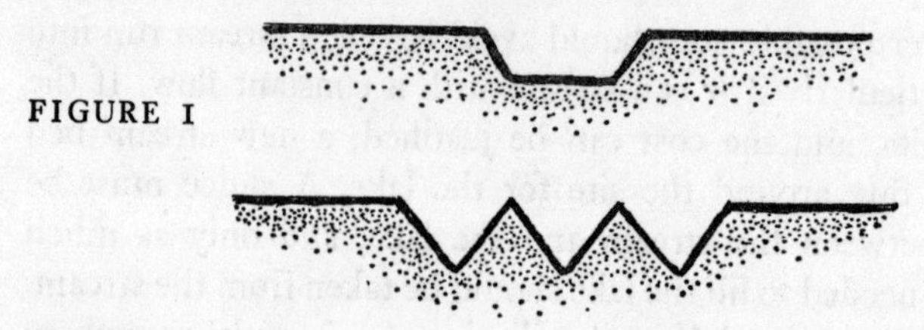

FIGURE 1

FIGURE 2

skimp this step because it's thought to be too much trouble or too expensive, would be foolish. The tangle of vegetation and turf must be moved clear of the site so that it is not incorporated into the dam.

Next, a drainage pipe must be laid through the base of the dam, and a sluice built. From now on, we had better call the sluice the 'monk', and later I will go into the details of how this sort of sluice is built. But first, the drainage pipe itself.

If you look at Figure 3 you see the stream in its original bed. Parallel with this stream, a ditch is dug which is just wide enough and deep enough to hold the pipes. At Two Lakes, with only a very small streamlet, we found that a pipe with a diameter of 30 cm was sufficient. The monk's aperture and the pipe are both 30 cm and they are used only for taking away water when the lake is emptied. The regular through flow of the stream, if any, is taken away by the overflow or overspill. The dimensions of the pipes must therefore depend on the feeder stream of the lake. The pipes can be concrete, or there are on the market now very cheap and durable pipes made from plastic or other new materials.

After the pipes have been laid (again look at the last sketch) the movement of the machines may disconnect them, though you can prevent this happening by driving posts in on both sides of the pipes so that they are firmly wedged. The whole row of pipes must have a gentle fall downstream. The posts can be left in permanently as they will not effect the dam.

Now, on the upstream end of this pipeline, the lake end, you must dig a hole for the foundation of the monk. Plan the foundation on quite a large scale, as the more substantial it is, the safer it will be. . . . Much depends on the nature of the ground. If it

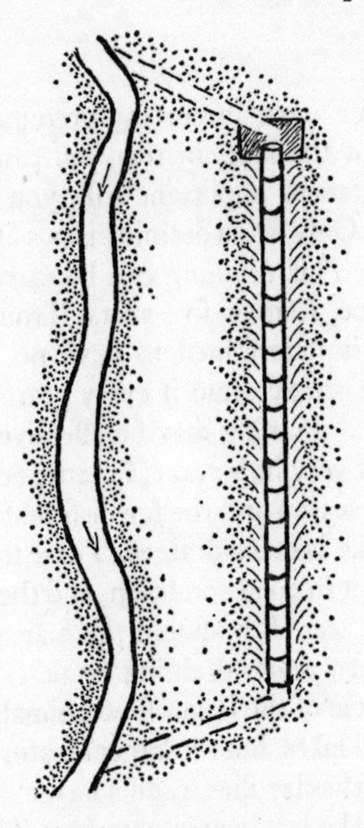

FIGURE 3

is hard clay a foundation one metre thick will do but if it is soft, you should dig far enough down to reach a firm bottom, and this may be more easily said than done. I have seen sites which could be classed as bottomless. However, to give an average example: a monk of three metres in height in soft ground should stand on a concrete foundation of at least two metres cubed, that is to say two metres by two metres by two metres. I have spelt it out so that there can be no mistake. Once again there must be no skimping. If the foundations of the monk are not strong enough, the thing will tilt and the boards will not slide up and down properly in the frame. The concrete for the foundation should not be too wet because water will seep into it from the surrounding soil. Furthermore, while the concrete is being shovelled into the hole, reinforcing iron rods must be pushed into it before it hardens, and these iron rods must stick out to the full height of the monk so that the monk and the foundation will be interlocked. Allow sufficient time for the concrete foundation to set and then you can get on with the construction of the monk itself.

The Monk

The monk is your most important prerequisite. It gives you physical control of the lake, in that you can regulate the level of the water and, more important still, you can drain the lake when you need to. Only when draining is possible can the management be efficient. This draining can be carried out every year, or every two, three, four or five years. Trout fisheries – where the management is determined to have no species other than trout in their lake – may drain it every year. On a put and take fishery such annual draining may be effective in as much as the natural food is not very important; because nearly all fish stock is caught during the season and the few fish that remain can be collected when the lake is being drained. These trout can be put into stewponds and kept in good condition, and then returned into the lake the following year. But should the management depend on natural feeding, then yearly draining would cause harm by interrupting the life cycle of the larger food animals. Plankton thrives in annually drained lakes, but the larger creatures such as nymphs of the damsel and the day flies, caddis larvae, shrimps, and some of the snails, would be lost in great numbers. The main purpose of draining such trout lakes would be to control the coarse fish.

Of course, activities such as repairing banks and sluices, removing mud, and removing snags which have fallen into the water are more easily accomplished with the lake empty. After the coarse fish have been removed, the remaining trout can be checked and all fish with faults destroyed while the healthy and well formed ones are kept. The ideal fishery has at least two lakes, which are never drained at the same time so that there is always somewhere to keep the fish which come out of the empty lake if there are no stewponds.

Last, but certainly not least, is the fact that the lake bottom is rejuvenated by being exposed to the air. If the lake is old, and has a quantity of mud, the frost must be allowed to bite into it. As the mud becomes drier and drier, the winter gales will whirl great clouds of black dust high into the air and carry them away. When, before the spring sets in, the lake is filled with water once more, it is a different lake and for several years to come it can provide ideal living conditions for numberless creatures.

This rather lengthy explanation of the benefits of being able to drain a lake, underlines the importance of a sluice which will work efficiently and is relatively simple and cheap to construct. The monk shown in Figure 4 best meets these requirements. It

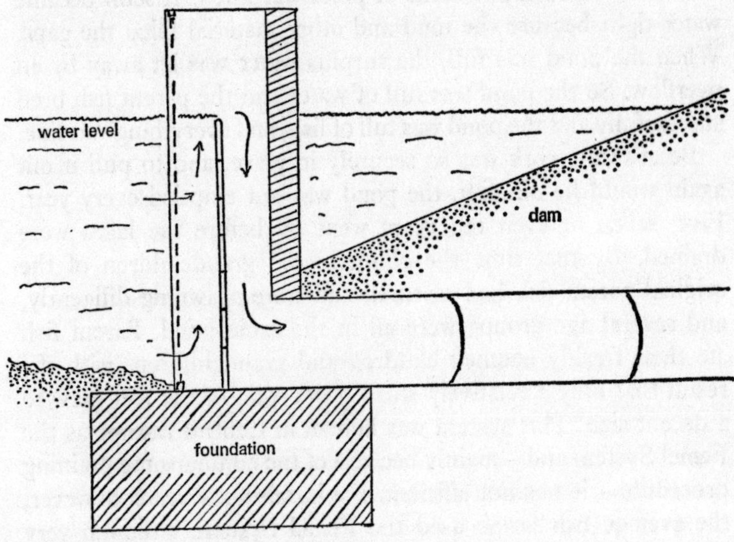

FIGURE 4

is interesting that through the centuries, people with an inventive turn of mind have evolved other methods but so far none have replaced the monk or even altered it significantly. Why was it invented, and how did it come by its name?

Some chroniclers hold that fish farming dates from about 800 to 1000 years ago. Others set the date even earlier – as far back as 2000 years in some Asian countries, and there is evidence to show that it was not very efficiently managed in those days. The fish farmers of that time kept some pairs of fish in small ponds and used the offspring of these fish for food. When the pond was very small they even fed their fish and when they wanted a few for dinner, they just netted them out of the pond. Then somebody wanted to get all the fish out of the pond and realized the best way to do this was to drain it.

Czechoslovakia, a country with a long history of fish culture, possesses ancient records of fish farming. In these rceords, written in Latin, we find the first mention of draining ponds and lakes. There is a description of a drainage pipeline underneath the dam and a large block of wood used as a cork to prevent the water from draining out through the pipe. Like a cork in a bottle this wedge-shaped block of wood fitted exactly into the opening of the pipeline in the lakeside of the dam. This was easy to instal before the lake or pond was filled. It soon became water-tight because the mud and other material filled the gaps. When the pond was full, the surplus water was let away by an overflow. So the pond was full of water and the parent fish bred successfully and the pond was full of fish, and everything was fine.

Because the cork was so securely in place, and to pull it out again would be difficult, the pond was not emptied every year. Five, seven or even ten years went by before the lakes were drained. By that time the children and grandchildren of the original parent fish had matured and were spawning diligently, and several age groups were all in the same pond. Parent fish ate their freshly hatched children and grandchildren, with the result that only a relatively small proportion of the fish grew to a decent size. This system was known in Central Europe as the Femel System and – mainly because of the cumbersome draining procedure – it was not efficient. For hundreds of years, however, the average fish farms used the Femel System, although very large farms were already trying to keep the different age groups in separate ponds.

It is almost unbelievable that there are even today a few people constructing lakes and building into them the old fashioned cork. What held true of the monastery fish farms of the past, holds true of the angling waters of today: corks are hopelessly inefficient and belong in a museum.

I have had the privilege of witnessing the draining of ponds where a cork was in operation (see Figure 5). One occasion in

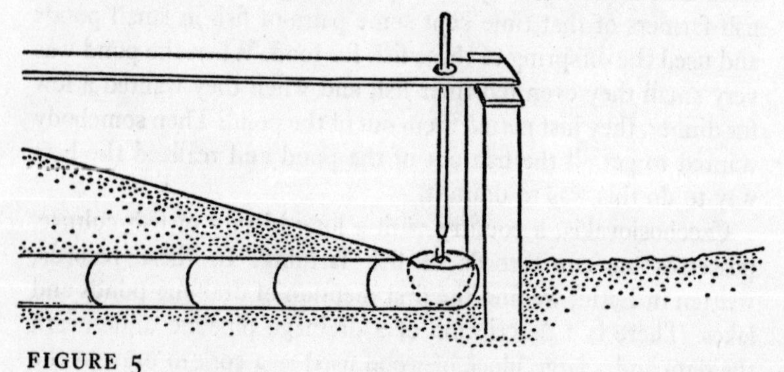

FIGURE 5

particular sticks in my mind. The cork had an iron ring attached to it, and onto the ring a long pole which could be pulled up by a man standing on a platform above. There were determined efforts at pulling up the pole and eventually the cork was loosened and came out, and the water rushed through the pipes underneath the dam and out on the other side to form quite a stream. After a while the water no longer ran at full bore and quickly diminished to a very modest flow. The enormous suction force of the water through the inflow had lodged branches and other debris in the pipe. We could see nothing when we looked into the pipeline from the outflow end, but the old foreman had experience of this sort of thing, and after poking around in the pipe with a hook attached to a long pole, he dislodged the obstructions and the water began to run freely. But soon the flow diminished again, and again the hook on a pole were brought into play. Subsequently, all through the day, there were periods when the pipe became blocked and clearing it took quite some time and effort. On the following day one process of clearing took several hours.

In fairness to the cork system, I must say that I have seen a very isolated lake emptied by this system and everything went smoothly. The lake had no trees near by and was surrounded by meadows, so the chance of debris falling into it was slight. No stream ran into it, and the water supply was from rain and drainage from the surrounding land. The Germans call such ponds '*Himmelsteiche*'; roughly translated this means water from heaven. But there aren't all that many *Himmelsteiche*. Most lakes and ponds have trees near by and some branches inevitably fall into the water.

Some fish farms place baskets over the mouth of the pipe to keep back the debris and fish. This is an improvement, but only temporary because the basket eventually becomes blocked up as well.

I know a man who constructs the occasional lake and, for some obscure reason, instals the cork draining system. I asked him how he coped with the problem of emptying a lake using this system. He had a very simple up-to-date solution: in the case of a blockage he calls in a diver who can clear the pipe quite easily. Of course! After this interesting discussion I telephoned a firm that hires out divers by the hour to ask about costs. First the diver's travelling expenses must be paid, according to the distance, the least amount payable being £11. Then each hour was charged at a rate of £7. These prices held good a while ago, and will certainly have increased. Now, it can take many days to empty a lake of five to ten hectares, and a blockage in the pipe can occur at any time, so it would be reasonable to require that there should be a diver in attendance the entire time. The pounds would mount up to a startling total and would soon show this modern solution to be hopelessly uneconomical.

It can, therefore, be said that the cork system is not efficient when a lake is being emptied. And that is not the only black mark against it. These are the other disadvantages:

1. It offers no possibility of drawing water off at differing levels in the lake, because once the cork is pulled out the water is drained only from the lowest level.
2. The flow of the water cannot be regulated and there can be no predetermined amount of water drawn away.
3. The water is always drawn off at pressure, with the result that the fish are sucked into the pipe and have a rough passage through it, often suffering damage.
4. Because there is no practical method of securing the cork, anyone who wants to (vandals most probably), can lift it out when nobody is around. This isn't easy but it can and has been done.

The leading fish farmers in the Middle Ages were the monks. There is no actual record of the events leading to their invention of the sluice but we can easily imagine their having tired of all the difficulties of the cork system. The sluice, which bears their name, must have been nearly perfect from the beginning, for, with few modifications it is still in use on countless fish farms and angling waters today.

After that aside on the purposes and history of the monk, we can return to the actual construction. In areas where the weather conditions are temperate this can be of brickwork. But in parts of the country where thick ice forms on ponds in winter, monks have been known to move on their foundations and the construction should be of solid concrete.

The walls must be at least 30 cm thick, solid, and with reinforcing irons in the centre of each wall. If the lake is going to

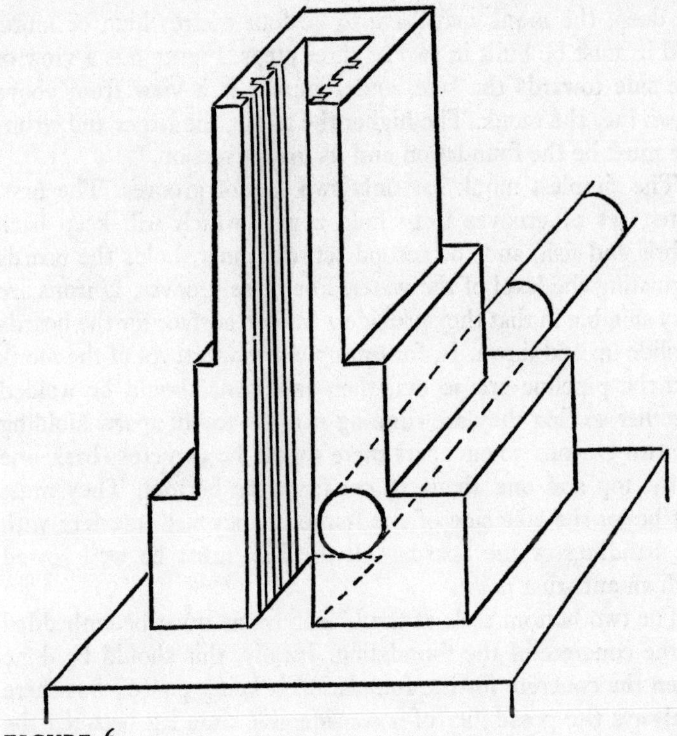

FIGURE 6

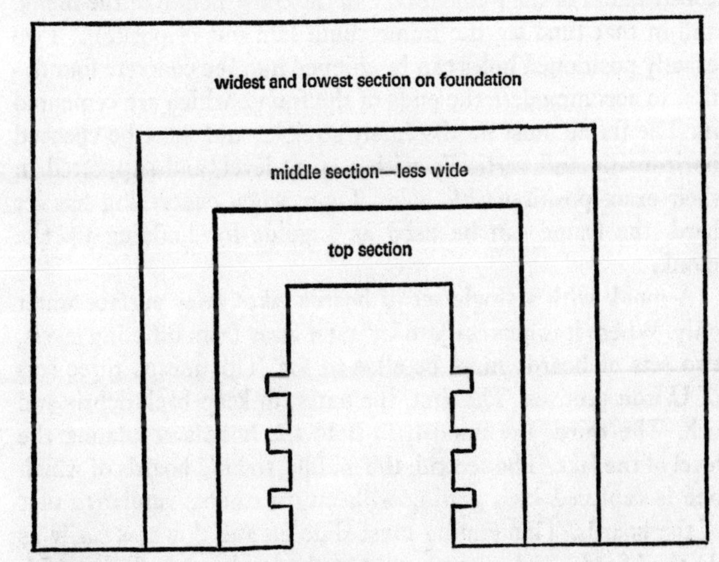

FIGURE 7

be deep, the monk may have to be four metres high or more, and it must be built in two or three steps. Figure 6 is a view of the side towards the lake, and Figure 7 is a view from above down into the monk. The higher the monk, the larger and stronger must be the foundation and its lowest section.

The simplest monk has only two sets of grooves. The first, outer, set of grooves is to hold a grid which will keep back debris and fish, and the second set, the inner, holds the boards regulating the level of the water. For these grooves, U irons are very suitable in that they provide a smooth surface for the boards to slide up and down. If, for example, the apertures of the monk and the pipeline are 30 cm, then two irons should be welded together so that they are running parallel 30 cm apart. Holding the two U irons 30 cm apart there should be two cross bars, one at the top and one about 10 cm from the bottom. They must not be on the lake side of the frame or they will interfere with the handling of the boards. All the iron must be well coated with an anti-rust paint.

The two bottom ends of the U iron frame must be embedded in the concrete of the foundation. Ideally, this should be done when the concrete for the foundation is being poured but there is always the possibility of a considerable time lag between the construction of the foundation and the construction of the monk, and in that time lag the frame could lean out of position. Two exactly positioned holes can be chipped into the concrete foundation to accommodate the ends of the frame, which are cemented in. The frame must be absolutely straight, and must be checked horizontally and vertically with a spirit-level, and supported in their exact position with poles. Later, when everything has set hard, the frame can be used as a guide for building up the monk.

A monk with a single set of boards takes away surface water only. Where it is necessary to let water away from differing levels, two sets of boards must be allowed for. This means three sets of U iron grooves. The first, the outer, to keep back debris and fish. The third, the inmost, to hold the boards regulating the level of the lake. The second, the middle, to hold boards of which one is replaced by a grating with measurements similar to that of the boards. This grating must slide up and down as easily as do the boards, and it can be put at the level at which you wish

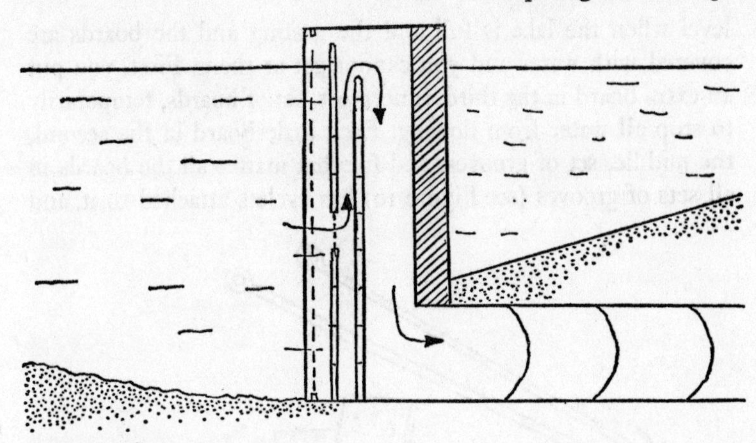

FIGURE 8

to draw off water (see Figure 8). If, for example, you want to draw water off from the bottom of the lake, you slide the grating down to the bottom of the second or middle set of grooves, and you slide the boards down to rest above the grating. The water flows through the grating at the bottom and up and over the third, inmost, section, down through the monk and out through the pipeline (see Figure 9). If you position the grating half-way up, you let water away from the middle layer of water. But always, the actual water level of the lake is governed by the height of the boards in the third, innermost, set of grooves.

You may well be wondering how you can alter the draw off

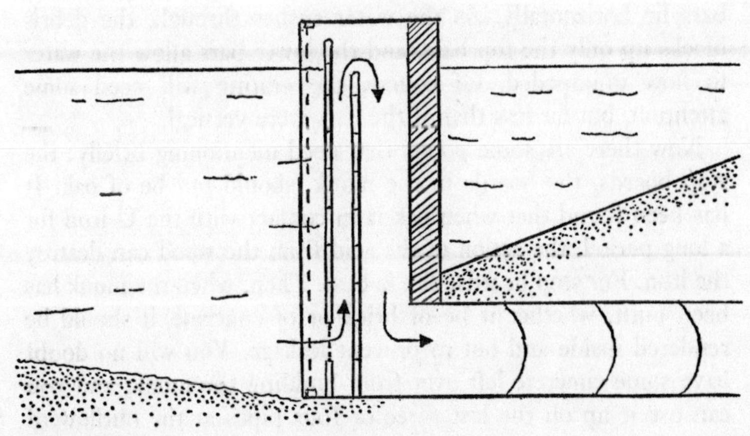

FIGURE 9

level when the lake is full and the grating and the boards are covered with water and you cannot get at them. First, you put an extra board in the third, innermost, set of boards, temporarily to stop all water from flowing. Each little board in the second, the middle, set of grooves, and for that matter all the boards in all sets of grooves (see Figure 10) has eyelets attached to it, and

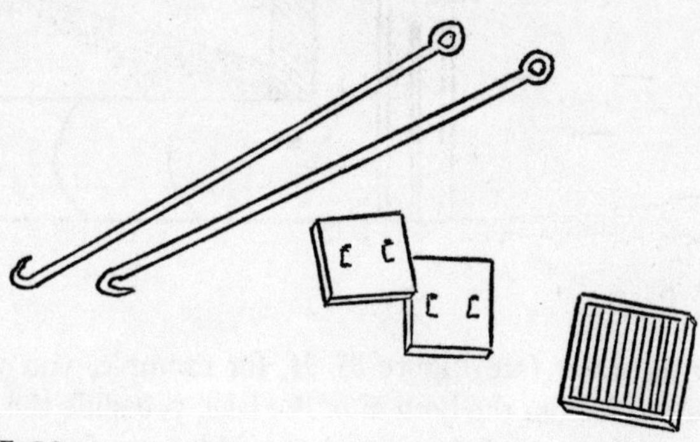

FIGURE 10

systematically, with a long hook iron, you draw up all the boards, and draw up the grating, which you then reset at the desired draw off level. Replace all boards on the grating, and then remove the top board from the third, innermost, section, so that the water flows again.

The measurements of the grating should be square so that the bars of the grating can be in a horizontal or a vertical position. When the lake is emptied the grating can be placed so that the bars lie horizontally. As the water rushes through, the debris blocks up only the top bars, and the lower bars allow the water to flow unimpeded. Of course, the grating will need some attention, but far less than if the bars were vertical.

Now there are some points that need mentioning briefly: the stop boards, the boards in the monk, should not be of oak. It has been found that when oak is in contact with the U iron for a long period, the action of the acid from the wood can destroy the iron. For stop boards, elm is best. Then, when the monk has been built, whether it be of brick or of concrete, it should be rendered inside and out to prevent leakage. You will no doubt have some concrete left over from building the monk, and you can use it up on the last three or four pipes at the outflow of the pipeline. It is as well to have them bedded with as much

above The boards have been inserted in the monk and the level of the lake is slowly rising.

right The end of the outflow pipe coming from the monk underneath the dam, must be set in solid concrete, to eliminate the danger of the pipes being pushed away when the lake is emptied.

left The bulldozer is the most useful machine for building the dam, especially for giving the dam the correct angles.

below The final job for the bulldozer is to level out all unevenness on the dam preparatory for seeding with grass or turfing.

concrete as possible. The reason is that should you have to open the monk, to the full capacity of the pipes, in an emergency, the enormous force of the water rushing through the pipes might shift the last ones with the result that some, if not all, of the dam would be washed away.

Here again I have had personal experience. As a young man I worked in Norway. Norway has a lot of rocks and not much soil, so when my boss constructed a small dam, it consisted mostly of rocks that we could manhandle into position, and soil was used only to fill the spaces between them. When the lake was three-quarters full, the seepage of water through the dam washed all the soil away and, on the offside of the dam, the escaping water looked like a thousand little fountains. We realized that at any moment something would go wrong and my boss told us to open the sluice fully and let the water out quickly. The tremendous rush of water through the pipes forced the last one right out of the dam, which collapsed within a matter of minutes, a wall of water shooting right down the valley into the fjord. It was fortunate that there were no houses below, and that there was no serious accident. The only damage was a number of broken birch and spruce trees, and a few deep gullies in the turf.

When you are constructing a dam you should try to make allowances for even the most improbable things that can go wrong. Remember Jenkins' Law: What Can Go Wrong Will Go Wrong.

For example, if the water of the lake is acid, it will be a great help if lime or chalk is packed around the monk. Acid water eats into concrete and the lime or chalk will slow up this action.

One last point: during hot summers when the water supply is dangerously low, remember that any leakage through the boards in the monk can be checked. Get some coarse coal ash and trickle it slowly into the water in front of the boards; the suction of the escaping water will pull the ash particles into the gaps that are causing the leaks. First some larger bits will become jammed, then finer particles will become stuck, and suddenly the leakage stops. It works like magic. The ash, however, must be absolutely dry, and if possible still hot, so that it will expand in the water. Many of these small leakages can be stopped in seconds by this dodge, but at first they are not permanently sealed. However, if you do this two or three times, you will probably succeed in stopping the leak for good.

A monk need not necessarily be made of bricks or concrete. It can be made entirely out of wood (see Figure 11.) which would be quite adequate on a short-term basis for coarse fish

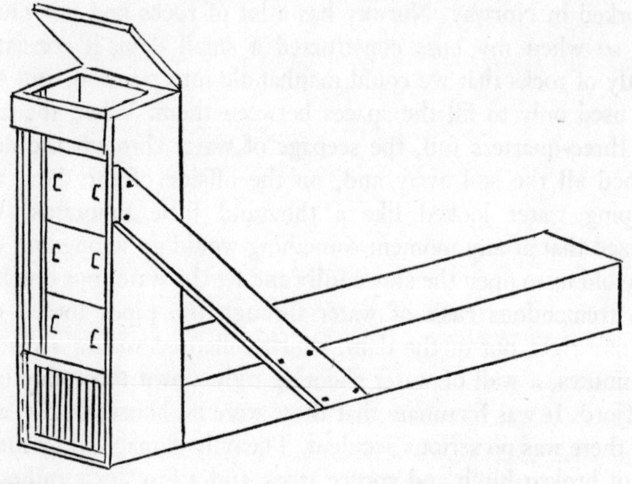

FIGURE 11

lakes where the deepest part of the water is under two metres. Equally it would do for a stewpond for bringing on a few thousand fish. It is cheap and very easy to construct, but of course wood, however well preserved, will only last for a limited time when all parts of the monk are not permanently immersed in water.

So, your monk has been built, and all concrete and mortar has had the time to become hard. Now, you must dig a ditch on the downstream or outlet end of the pipes towards the stream and joining it. Then on the upstream, or the lake side, or more simply, in front of the monk (*and of course there are no stop boards or gratings in the monk at this stage*) you dig another ditch towards the stream, so that the stream is directed through the monk, into the pipes, out of them, and back into the original stream bed. (See Figure 12 on following page.)

Now you must block off the old stream bed so that it can dry out. It will soon be filled in when the dam building commences. Something important must not be forgotten. You will remember that the site on which the dam will sit had to be cleared of all

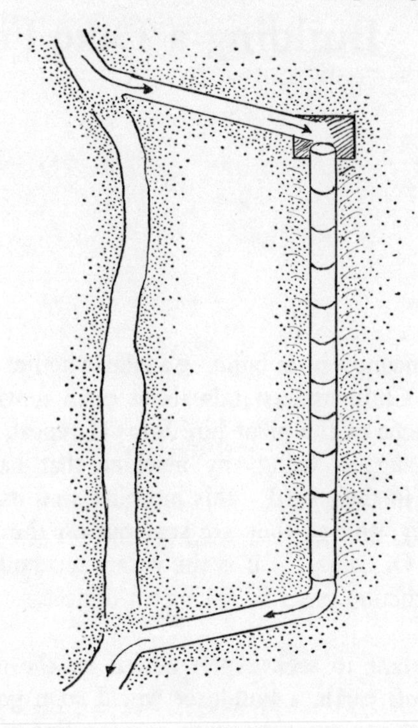

FIGURE 12

turf, shrubs and trees; likewise, the stream bed, where the foundation of the dam will be, must be cleared completely of all vegetation. When this is done, everything is ready and waiting for the earth moving machines to start their work.

3 Building a Lake Fishery

The more someone who is building a lake, whether an individual or a Fishing Club, understands about earth moving machines the better. Some of the plant hire firms (I repeat, *some*) have a tendency to suggest using any machine that happens to be standing idle in their yard – this machine, and its driver, have to earn money, and so they are sent out on the first job that comes along. Of course, if it is the wrong machine it will push up the construction costs by taking an unnecessarily long time over the job.

It is important to seek expert advice on the nature of the terrain. On soft earth, a bulldozer would soon get stuck, so a dragline, which can stand on mats, is safer. But with a dragline the soil may have to be moved several times (some machine operators call this procedure 'haymaking'), and consequently the costs escalate. Again, a bulldozer becomes uneconomic when the soil must be pushed over a long distance; a scraper would be more economic. New machines are being brought into use all the time, and it is therefore relatively easy to find one that is perfectly suited for a particular job. Always bearing in mind the work to be accomplished and the conditions of the job (i.e. how much room there is to manoeuvre in), it is a good idea to make a number of enquiries from a number of different firms.

The work can be undertaken in two ways. First, a job can be done under contract. You begin by getting estimates from different contractors. Naturally, you will be attracted by the lowest estimate – who wouldn't be? – but this low estimate may mean a shoddy job. On the other hand, you must not assume that the highest estimate will give the best results. Your safest course is to find out which firm has the best reputation. If a contractor undertakes to do a job for a certain sum of money, he will have allowed for the possibility of getting bogged down with his machine, or of other time wasting incidents. If everything goes without a hitch, the contractor will do very well, but I have known many contracted jobs where the terrain produced one nasty surprise after another, and in sticking to the agreed price the firm made a heavy loss. It is therefore understandable that a contractor will try to protect himself by estimating a price that will cover every potential. It is worth remembering this and also that it is unwise to sign a contract for a low estimate where there are many 'we are not responsibles' in very small print.

The other way to undertake the building is to hire machines by the hour or week and to organize everything yourself. Machines may become bogged down for a whole day, or they may be unable to work because of bad weather, or there may be delays because materials have not been delivered in time . . . all this you must pay for. On the other hand, should everything go smoothly, you get the work done well and cheaply.

A good example of this method was the construction of the Spring Lake at Two Lakes. The site of the proposed lake was a little valley, overgrown with rhododendron, willow, bramble and reeds. I asked two contractors – on different days, of course – to look at the site and to give me an estimate. I showed them the plans. I took them round the site. I explained in detail what I wanted done. They went home to do their sums and after a fortnight I received their estimates. One contractor wanted £2000, and the other, for the same job, £800. They both stated in detail what was to be done, and they both said the job would take about a month to complete. It was an interesting difference in price. Their mistake was that they both quoted a month as the time it would take to carry out the work.

As it was, we hadn't that sort of money to spare in those days, so we asked around and found out what bulldozers cost an hour, multiplied that by the month, and approached a third firm. I hired a bulldozer by the hour, promised the driver a juicy bonus, supervised everything myself, and the total cost for building a very nice lake was £300. But we were lucky. We did not come across difficult soil, and there were very few and minor setbacks. The driver was interested in what we were doing, and he handled his bulldozer with skill and elegance. To our delight he completed the work in a month.

Of course, in fairness to the first two contractors, neither of them knew that the site for Spring Lake was going to be easy; that's something you only know for sure when the job is completed. Their estimates therefore, had to be for more than my £300, although £2000 was overdoing it a bit.

Nobody these days will get a lake built for £300 – the value of money has changed too much for that. But the ratios don't alter, and that is what is important: the cost in relation to the time spent and the work accomplished.

The more suitable the site, the cheaper the undertaking. Where the shape of the land is such that the earth moving machinery has only to provide the finishing touches, so to speak, the lake can be built at a very reasonable cost indeed. The most perfect site I have ever seen is very near the River Test. When, during the last century, a railway line was built along the valley, the gravel for the railway embankment was dug out from a nearby hill. The result was a hollow of about three hectares with a ten metre gap in the bank through which the gravel was hauled out. During the work, two small springs were unearthed, and the water was allowed to flow through the ten metre gap down to the River Test. When, 150 years later, the then owner wanted to build a lake, he had a bulldozer fill the gap, and in two days a three hectare lake was created at the smallest imaginable cost. Of course, a monk was built before the small dam was pushed across the gap.

Although you may have not had the luck to acquire a site such as the one just described, you have at least obtained a site. Plans have been drawn up; all the authorities have given their permissions; you have prepared your site; and you have built your monk. The big day has come when the earth moving machines arrive on the site. The drivers of the machines are eager to begin work, but they have probably never been involved in constructing a lake. Most of their time has been spent in building motorways. So all eyes are trained on you. But do you know what you have to do now? You may have called in an expert, with a high score of success in lake building to his credit, in which case you can leave everything to him. At a price, of course. But we assume that you will supervise the work yourself, and that you will find it always interesting and at times as nerve-racking and exciting as a survival course.

The machines start by building the dam, and if the lie of the land permits, the soil for this should be taken from the sides of the valley where the lake is to be. By taking the dam material from the sloping sides, the lake will be made larger, and it can be shaped to make interesting fishing. You don't want a saucer-shaped lake which would be both uninteresting and wasteful of opportunities. This is another stage of the project at which mistakes can be made. I know several small lakes which have been constructed without any play of imagination. They are rectangular, even square, and viewed from a nearby hill, they look for all the world like large stewponds. No wonder the fishermen have nicknames for them – 'tennis courts', etc. It would not have cost extra to give the banks of these lakes a different shape during construction and they would look more attractive and accommodate more anglers.

Figure 13 shows how lakes with about the same acreage of

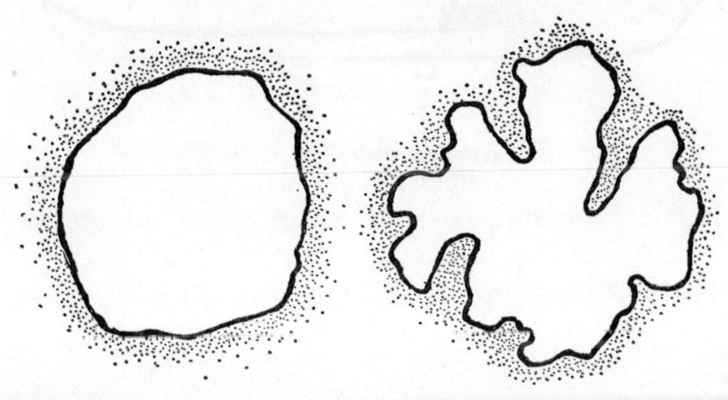

FIGURE 13

water but differently shaped can give the angler the impression of being alone. Through clever planting of trees and shrubs, another angler may be very close to him and yet not be visible.

Figure 14 (on p. 40) demonstrates how the bulldozer works. If the dam measures, say 50 metres wide at the base, then from the start the bulldozer should push over the whole width of those 50 metres, and, as the dam grows higher and narrower, it must still travel over the entire width of the dam, layer by layer. The machines weigh many tons, and with their enormous weight, especially when they are in motion, they are consolidating the dam continuously.

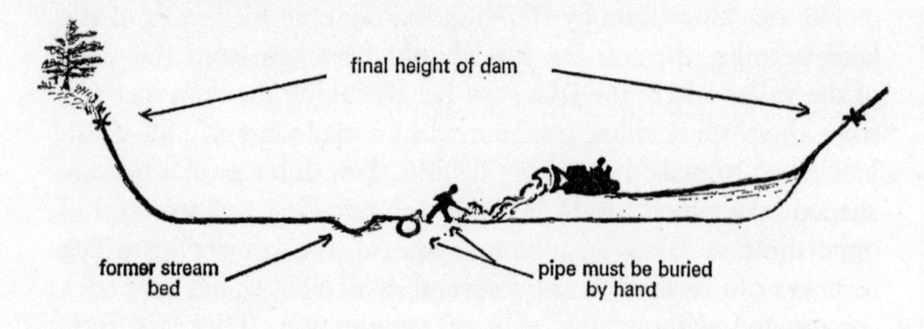

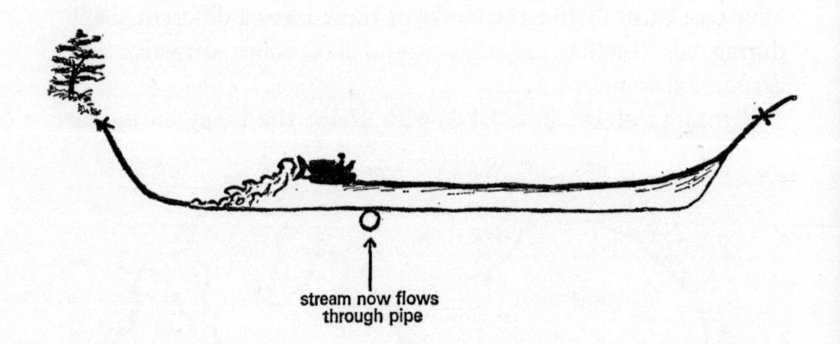

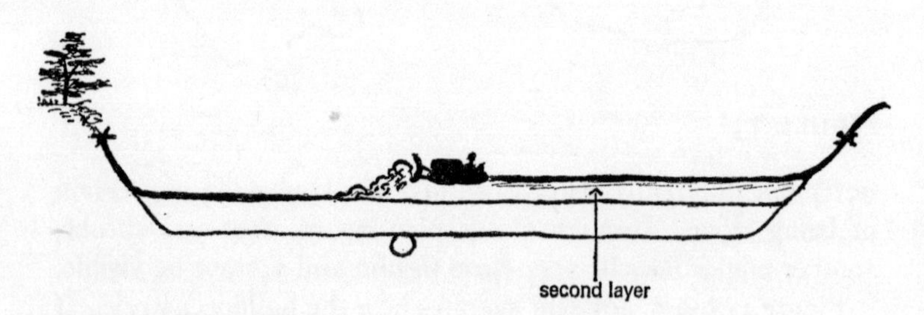

FIGURE 14

The depth of the first layer of dam building material depends on the terrain. If the ground is very soft the bulldozer will need three to four metres, sometimes even more, of dry soil under it so that it won't be bogged down. Travelling back and forth, the machines will compress the dry material more and more into the soft soil below, and gradually the work progresses across the valley. When the machine comes closer and closer to the line of pipes, you have to watch out. The bulldozer itself may be more than eight metres away from the line of pipes, but already the soil in front of it is moving closer to the pipeline. The enormous pressure of the advancing material may push the pipes apart and block them up, with the result that the stream cannot flow through them, and the water will rise quickly on the lake side of the dam and make work difficult, if not impossible. Even the posts which have been driven into the ground will not hold. I have even seen pipes which have been laid in concrete for their whole length, burst open when the bulldozer was pushing soil several metres away.

What you must do is to stop the machine eight metres or more away from the pipeline. Then make the machine push its bladeful of soil at a reduced speed, travelling the last metres gently (if you can use the term gently for a bulldozer). Slowly, the operator lifts the blade and lets the soil fall down in front of his machine. Then, still travelling slowly, he reverses; only when he is twenty or more metres away from the pipeline can he let the machine go full blast. Closer to the pipeline the vibration would do damage. Then the bulldozer returns with another bladeful, and the procedure of lifting the blade slowly and letting the soil roll down slowly towards the pipes is repeated.

All the time, two or three men shovel the base earth further towards the pipeline, and eventually on to the pipes where they must tread it in firmly. When the pipes have been covered in this way with say, about three or four metres of soil, the bulldozer should drive slowly over the buried pipes and press the soil down. The machine can then start pushing soil again but for the first twenty or thirty journeys across the buried pipes it should be driven slowly. After that, the pipes should be embedded firmly in the consolidated soil and should no longer have any tendency to move.

While all this work is going on *over* the pipeline, it is a good thing if you go and look *through* the pipeline every now and then. If you can see through to daylight on the other end, everything is all right. But you can tell very soon if the pipes have shifted and if this happens you have to dig up the lot, realign them, and again cover the whole pipeline with soil packed down well. So the more care that is taken the more time (and money) will be saved.

There is always the question, 'What material should be used for building a dam? Can it be ordinary black soil, sand or clay?' The answer is that the more waterproof the material is the better, so that clay becomes the obvious choice. Clay that was deposited by the upheavals of nature eons ago, is generally speaking firm and impermeable. However, when a bulldozer or excavator breaks it up and shifts it, it often becomes soggy, especially after rain, and a dam built completely of this loose clay, has a tendency to slip away. In Czech literature dealing with fish pond construction, it is stated (for the first time in print) that pure clay is not the ideal material for building dams. These days, therefore, most dams are constructed with a clay core, but the sides are made up of whatever material happens to be handy on the site.

We are not, of course, discussing here the construction of dams for larger reservoirs. At the moment, the construction of any lake holding more than five million gallons of water comes under the Reservoir Act, and is an entirely different matter. We are discussing dams for holding back water over a few hectares. In dam construction, especially on the smaller scale by private individuals or angling clubs with limited capital, there is often very little choice in the material available. Sometimes it is mostly sand, but a dam ought not to be constructed of sand alone. Generally speaking the machines will be moving a mixture of soils; so long as this mixture, does not contain less than 50% of clay particles, the seepage will be tolerable. If the angles of the dam slopes are correct, it will not endanger the dam. (Incidentally, if the clay content of the material is about 50% throughout the dam, then it is not even necessary to have a clay core at the centre.)

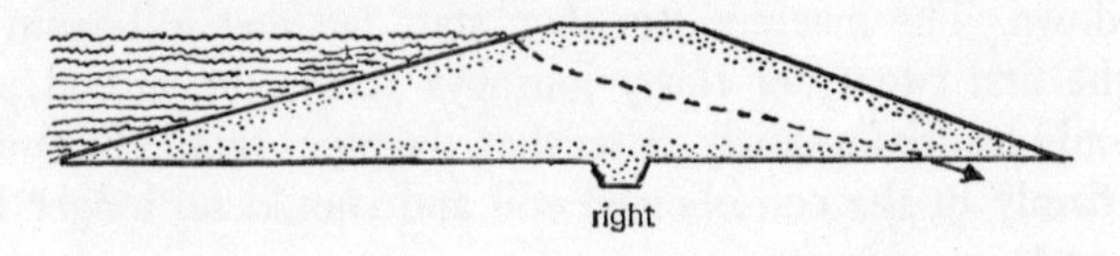

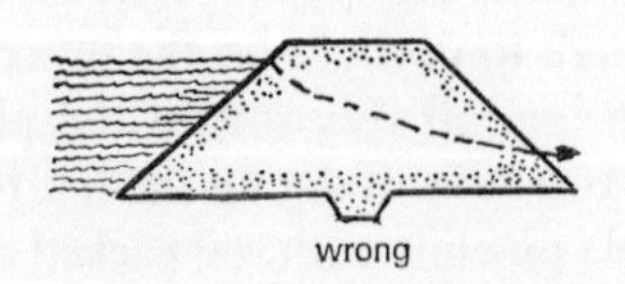

FIGURE 15

What about chalk? It would be most unsatisfactory to have a dam built of chalk which is porous and would be subject to excessive seepage. But in spite of clay cores and clay content all earthen dams suffer some degree of seepage. Figure 15 shows how the seepage works, and the photograph facing page 64 shows a dam which has been broken by it.

The slope of the sides of the dam on the water side should be 1 in 4, and on the off side 1 in 3. Some contractors build dams with steeper slopes: less material has to be moved and that makes the dam cheaper. I prefer a dam to be as safe as possible, even if the construction costs more. After all, the dam is there for a lifetime, perhaps many lifetimes, and when there are heavy rains and floods, and strong gales are whipping the water into waves, it is a good feeling to know that the dam sits wide and strong on its site. You can never overdo the width of the dam, and the shallowness of the slope of the sides. A rule in dam building is that the width at the top should be equal to the height of the dam. In other words, a five metre high dam is five metres wide across the top. Should money be no object and the material available, a dam ten metres wide at the top, with correspondingly gently sloping sides, but only five metres high, would be ideal. However, consideration of construction costs forces us to work just within the accepted safety figures. To go below these figures is to ask for trouble. Water, just as much as fire, is a dangerous thing to play with. Figure 16 gives the dimensions of a dam.

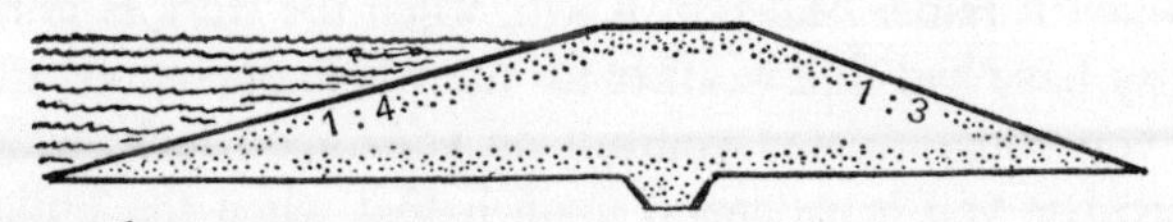

FIGURE 16

You have now settled the dimensions of the dam, you know what sort of soil you will have available and you have buried your concrete pipeline successfully. The bulldozer slogs on, pushing layer upon layer of soil from the sides of the valley across the dam. Under ideal conditions the proportions of the layers should be about as follows: the first layer should be roughly 3 to 4 metres high; the next layer can be less deep, say 2 to 3 metres. As the dam narrows towards the top, each layer is less wide than the layer below and we must remember to keep each layer in conformation with the slopes of the sides of the dam: an angle of 1 in 4 on the water side, and 1 in 3 on the off side. All the time the bulldozer is travelling to and fro it is pressing down the soil, consolidating it, layer by layer, and it is worth making sure that it covers the platform completely on each of its journeys for this compression of the soil is invaluable. If the machine were to push the soil to the final height of the dam all at once, and not layer by layer, there would be considerable settling, and the seepage would be greater.

When the required height of the dam has been reached, it will look very rough indeed. The bulldozer has now to shape the sides of the dam by starting on one side and driving vertically from the bottom to the top. Up and down, up and down, each time moving to its side only by the widths of its tracks. When the lake side of the dam has been finished, the other side should get the same treatment. This is the final consolidating of the dam which will now look rather odd with the thousands of track marks showing. It is at this stage that a skilful driver can perform a most elegant manoeuvre; he can drive backwards, and by backblading, as it's called, give the dam its final shape. The sides will be smooth, and the top can be made absolutely level. I have had bulldozer drivers who were so enthusiastic to show their skill, that they patiently levelled the top of the dam by conforming to a line of pegs which I had driven in and levelled with a spirit-level. It sounds a bit finicky, but if the top of the dam *is* absolutely level, with no little dips in it, puddles cannot form when it rains. And rain it will, when the work is finished. You may have had fine weather for the whole operation, and no doubt you congratulated yourself on your good luck, which is fatal because you can depend upon it that when the bulldozer roars away, the first drops of rain will patter down. If there are a few dips in the top of the dam, rain collects into puddles, and they overflow with the greatest glee, making gulleys in the sides of your beautiful new dam – deep gulleys. Once the grass grows, this won't happen. Of course, if the money is available, you can turf the sides of the dam at once. It isn't really all that expensive. Even at Two Lakes we have turfed new dams. As the result of one of my raising-of-the-water-level operations, we were faced with a considerable expanse of raw bank on Home Pool. My wife was rather plaintive about it all, and additionally, the beginning of the fishing season was only a few weeks away. Grass seed was no use with no time to grow, so we ordered turf. It was laid in three days, and the dam looked as though it had always been there: instant matured dam, with grass on the top and offside, and on the lake side down to the water's edge.

The total height of your completed dam should be around 50 to 60 centimetres above the highest water level of the lake. The larger the lake (remember that we are not discussing reservoirs), the greater this safety margin should be. The overflow, or overspill, will regulate the level of the lake, and this level must be a little below the top board of the monk. In other words, surplus water must always run off through the overflow, not through the monk.

One very important thing must never be forgotten. The machines must not dig deeper than the bottom of the monk, otherwise the lake can never be emptied one hundred per cent. This should be explained to the drivers. It must be horribly boring for a man to drive a machine back and forth all day without knowing the purpose and I have found during many lake construction operations that a talk with the drivers, as well as a generous tip, helps the whole business enormously. The driver will then also understand that the sides of the lake must slope towards the centre, the whole bottom of the lake must slope towards the dam and the monk must be at the lowest point to make the total draining of the lake possible. Drainage ditches can be dug from the sides towards a centre ditch, which in most cases will be the old stream. Figure 17 makes it look rather like a tree trunk with a few dry branches sticking out. Every effort should be made to arrange such a draining pattern.

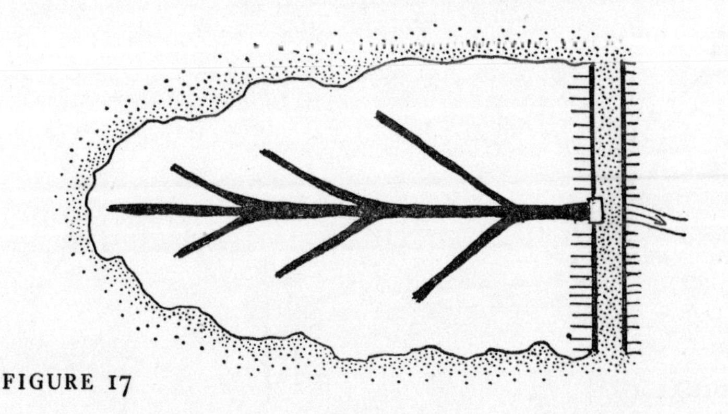

FIGURE 17

After considering the lie of the land, sticks should be driven into the ground to guide the machine operator. I go so far as to give the driver an informative little lecture: I explain that you must have total physical control over a lake, otherwise you will never get the best out of it. I explain how all the creepy-crawlies multiply in a newly flooded lake, and all that we can achieve if it is possible to have the bottom of the lake dry for mud control, weed removing, liming, fertilizing, and repairing. To build a lake is much more interesting than to build a motorway and many drivers become very enthusiastic often making their own suggestions about how things can be made easier or improved upon.

I remember one such driver particularly well. For various reasons we had to delay the construction of a lake until the late autumn. The rains had started already, and if circumstances had permitted I would have preferred to wait for the dry summer months. In all that wet, we had to work with masses of clay, and the clay stuck to everything, men and machines. One particularly miserable afternoon, as another dark rain cloud appeared above us, I shouted to the driver who was working his machine along the bottom of the lake that we had better knock off. The driver was a coloured immigrant from Mauritius, and after he had slid across the clay towards me, he said as he tried to shake the muck off his clothes and hands: 'And my father wanted me to become a doctor!' He was laughing in spite of everything. With helpers like that any project must be a success.

Well now, the next thing we must cope with is the overflow. Figure 18 gives a bird's-eye view of the location of the overflow.

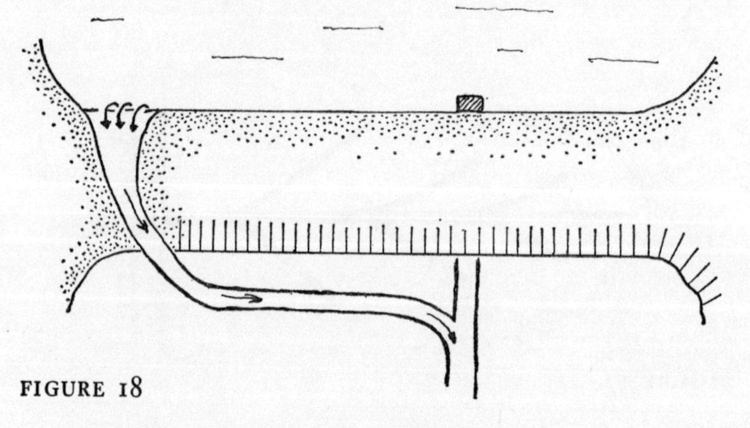

FIGURE 18

It is very important to choose the right location and then to construct the overflow correctly. Some fisheries use the monk as an overflow. In a stewpond on a trout farm or a growing-on pond on a carp farm, the monk often serves as an overflow and is used for draining the pond as well. In an angling lake of several hectares, and with a stream running through it to boot, it is dangerous to use the monk both as an overflow and for draining. The example from Two Lakes will serve as an explanation. All monks at Two Lakes have a 30 cm wide aperture, and the pipes adjoining the monk and running underneath the dam are also 30 cm in diameter. Should we decide to empty the lake, the pipes are able to cope with the normal volume of water in a few days. The purpose of the overflow is to cope with extra water.

The inflow stream at Two Lakes is generally a harmless trickle, and is only 30 cm wide. In autumn and winter there is a reasonable flow, just enough to keep all the lakes full. Should there be a low rainfall during the summer, the tiny stream dries up completely. People not concerned with fishery management look at our enormous overflow, which is four metres wide, and think it rather a joke. But the same people would not think it funny at all if they were to look at the stream where it flows into the lake and then look at the overflow on the other side of the lake, after weeks of really heavy winter rains. I have seen a dog fall into the stream and be swept away. The overflow runs in a torrent with such a roar that you have to shout to make yourself heard. You have to remember that there are occasions when the weather reports inform us that we are experiencing the worst floods for, say, 120 years: the overflows must be able to swallow such floods. Should the monks here at Two Lakes be used as overflows, they would never be able to swallow the surplus water at its maximum. This would only be possible if the monks were much wider, not 30 cm but 60 cm or more; then they would be proper skyscrapers and almost as expensive to build, and still there would be no assurance that they could cope with the very worst floods.

It is, therefore, reasonable to say that an overflow is essential. Furthermore, it must be very wide and very deep; its cubic dimensions must be several times larger than those of the monk. In short, it must be of such a size that it could swallow more water than could reasonably be expected.

If you look again at the last diagram, the overflow is located where the dam joins the side of the valley, because here the ground has not been disturbed by machines. If it were to be constructed half-way along the dam, between the sides of the valley, it would sit not on ground soil but on soil that has been moved there by the bulldozer, comparatively loose soil. The soil may have been consolidated by the bulldozer to some extent – you may have tested it by pushing a spade into it and found that the spade does not go in easily – but should you now construct a concrete overflow on it, there is the possibility that water will find a way to seep through below, or beside, the concrete construction. First a little moisture appears, and you are not unduly alarmed. A few days later there is a tiny trickle dribbling along. A few days later still there is a proper little flow 6 or 7 cm wide. When things get to this stage it is high time to sound the alarm, lower the water level of the lake and start repair work. If you don't, you may come one fine morning to look at your lake and find that water has ripped an enormous hole underneath the overflow and the lake has dropped several metres. And you can count yourself lucky if that entire section of the dam hasn't been washed away. My description of the possible disaster may seem rather melodramatic, but a horror story has greater impact than has the statement 'You may have trouble'.

So remember that the overflow must be built on virgin soil, soil that has not been disturbed by the machines. Of course there will still be seepage, the solid ground will allow the water to soak away, but nothing will collapse. The weight of the overflow will not shift on solid ground but that same weight on packed up soil is an untrustworthy and unholy affair.

The start of the operation is the digging of a channel 30 cm below the permitted future level of the lake. The digging should commence on the lake side and then slowly downwards in an arch towards the stream where it reappears out of the pipeline under the dam. Figure 19 (on p. 49) will help you to understand the construction. The width of the channel on the lake side of the dam should be about four metres, similar to what we have at Two Lakes. This channel can become narrower and deeper as it slopes down on the offside of the dam. The intake, the lake side, of the overflow must be so very wide to prevent the lake

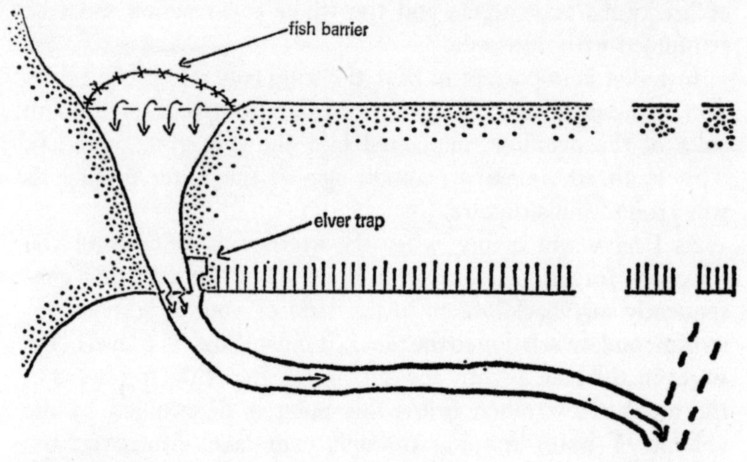

FIGURE 19

level rising suddenly, and also to provide for the installation of a fish barrier. This barrier not only prevents the fish from escaping, it also holds back debris. The wider the overflow intake, the less frequently the fish barrier needs to be cleared. This barrier can be made of finely meshed plastic net, and is like a semi-circular fence, one or two metres in front of the overflow, staked firmly into the lake bottom.

The object of digging out the soil to 30 cm below the lake level is to give room for the floor of the overflow to be made of thick concrete, nearly 30 cm thick; and this concrete floor must be extended a metre or more into the lake. Figure 20 demonstrates it in profile. The extension helps to prevent the water from finding a way under the concrete of the overflow. The sides of the overflow, right down to the back of the dam, can be made

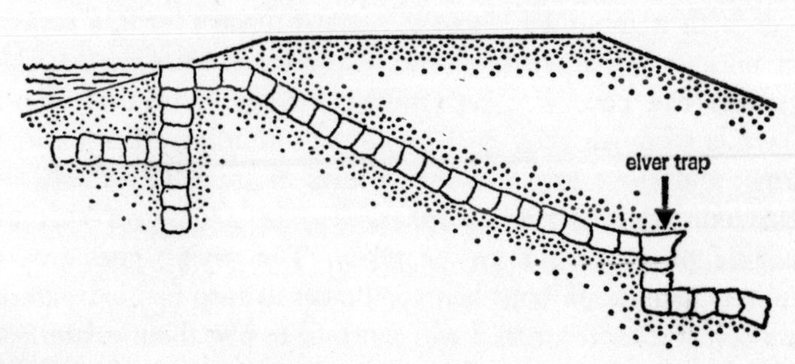

FIGURE 20

of brickwork or concrete and the whole construction must be reinforced with iron rods.

Just as it is important to have the solid concrete lip or extension, just described, it is equally necessary to have 'ears' on both sides of the overflow, implanted into the soil, right and left. This is an additional precaution against the water finding its way around the structure.

As I have said before, when the overflow is being built you must not forget that it governs the level of the lake and consequently any backflow on to the land of your neighbour upstream; and, in relation to the monk, it must allow for a level of the water in the lake slightly lower than the top of the top board in the monk. How much below this point is determined by the volume of water running through your lake. Moreover, the overflow is being built before the lake has started to fill with water. All the water the stream brings down is running through the open monk and the pipes underneath the dam. You could be in a vulnerable position at the time of building the overflow. Should it rain for weeks on end, the monk and the pipes might not be able to take all the water, and the level of the water in the lake would rise and continue to rise. If it should rise to the top of the dam and run over it, the dam would be washed away, which would be disastrous. When the stream flow is unpredictable, therefore it is advisable to build the overflow before the dam is constructed, and this is another good reason why lake building operations should be undertaken during the summer months.

Thinking up all the awful possibilities may seem unduly pessimistic but we are dealing with an element which can be as dangerous as fire when it gets out of control. I have had much to do with water and I have the greatest respect for it, a respect not untinged by fear. A harmless little crack showing a trickle of water can become a catastrophic torrent in no time at all. There is so much activity these days in building lakes and fish farms, and there are so many reports of incredibly foolhardy behaviour, that I must emphasise again and again that all possible precautions must be taken. The saying goes that a cautious man wears both belt and braces to keep up his trousers. Be a belt and braces man. I will continue to nag about calamities.

An interesting and useful refinement to the overflow is an

elver trap. This would only be necessary in trout fisheries, since these try to exclude all fish other than trout. (A coarse fishery, in most instances, welcomes the little eels as another sporting fish for its members.)

To prevent elvers from entering a trout lake, the elver trap is installed alongside the overflow. There must be at the foot of the overflow, a little waterfall of at least 60 cm in height. The elvers will try to climb up the waterfall, but at the top there is a protruding lip which the elvers cannot negotiate. When they try to find another way, they encounter a trickle of water which they follow, and it leads them into the trap where they can be collected and removed. The photograph of the Two Lakes elver trap facing page 65 gives an idea of how it works. You will see on the top of the trap a small pipe sticking out; this pipe supplies the trickle of water from the water that flows down the overflow. Don't have grass growing each side of the trap because, particularly when the grass is wet, the elvers can wriggle up it and manage to reach the lake. Plant conifer trees for several metres to the left and right of the trap, so that the needles will form a carpet which is impossible for the elvers to wriggle on.

There is another interesting and useful refinement that can be added when you have finished your overflow – the subject of yet another discussion!

Whenever it is decided to empty the lake, the monk will be opened and the water from the lake will run away through the pipes underneath the dam. Be it a trout or a coarse fish lake, it will be necessary to catch all the fish population. As board after board is taken out of the monk, the water level in the lake drops and when the last board is removed, the last of the water will drain away through the pipes and the fish are forced to go with it, otherwise they would be left high and dry. Now, this catching of the whole fish population of the lake can be the greatest fun, with the added pleasure of a nice financial return, or it can be a tiring, dirty, and not very productive chore. You have a man with a hand net placed at the outlet pipe. As the fish come floundering through the pipe, they fall into the net. Another man is ready to take over when the first man's net is full, and so it goes on, turn and turn about, with the netfuls of fish being put into containers standing near by. There must be another team removing the containers as they become full and replacing them. A considerable amount of water is slopped around and conditions become slippery; often the rush of water is so loud that everybody has to shout in order to be heard. It is fun, but the essence of the fun is that a lot of fish are being caught. Most people are quite happy with this rather primitive arrangement because they never have seen the same proceedings carried out more efficiently and with less mud and spilled water.

We have worked this primitive method at Two Lakes, and the last lake emptying operation we carried out was a blueprint of all the problems that can arise. We were emptying the Lower Lake, and from previous years' experiences, I know exactly when the last water would run out of the lake. I organised helpers and on a fixed day I pulled the last stop board out of the monk. All the fish which had congregated in front of the monk, started coming through the pipeline. The water was running fast and it was like a conveyor belt in a factory, with the fish coming through non stop and everybody bustling back and forth with buckets and baths full of fish and water. The fish were tench, of various sizes, and when we counted them later, their number was 82,000. A successful undertaking and worth a few thousand pounds.

But the work was tiring and dirty. The last bit of water always brings with it a quantity of mud, and the great number of fish in front of the monk splash about in the very shallow water and stir up the mud and the rotting leaves. All this muck flows with the fish through the pipeline and clogs up the nets, and, worst of all, it does the fish no good. Tench are very hardy and can stand a lot, but should there be roach, bream or some other coarse fish, quite a number would die.

It would be a great improvement if a trap were to be installed, such as is used on carp farms on the Continent, and we at Two Lakes mean to have one built. A wooden box, or much better a concrete box, is built as a continuation of the outlet pipes, a little below the level of the last pipe in the pipeline. The box has a slope so that it can be drained of water, and this means that the original stream bed must be a little lower. Now, the most important point. I have already said that the stream feeding the lake, or chain of lakes, should not flow through the lakes. Whenever possible, the stream should be led around the lakes in a new stream bed and must join the original stream bed below the last lake. The box trap installed below the outlet pipes must have access to fresh clean water, so that when the fish appear out of the pipeline they can be sorted from the mud and debris. A water supply can be led right into the box from the stream flowing around the lakes. You will see what I mean when you look at Figure 21 which shows how the whole thing

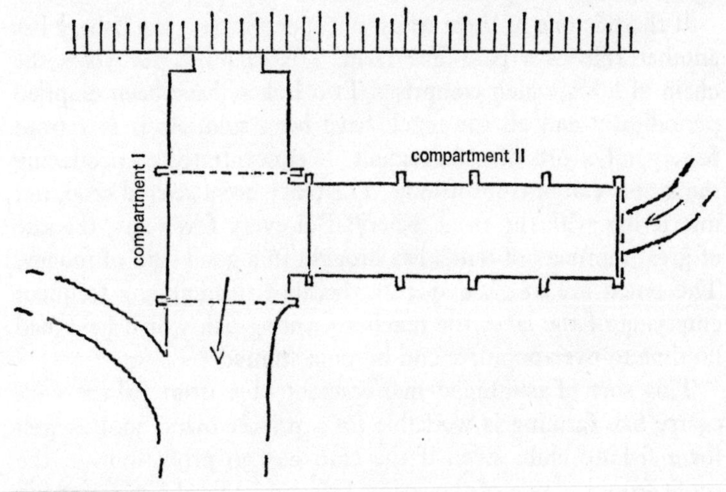

FIGURE 21

works. The fish are washed through the pipeline into Part 1 of the trap. Part 2 continually gets clean water, which flows over the stop board into Part 1. The dirty water from the lake mixed with the clean water flows through a grid out of Part 1 and away. All fish caught in Part 1 are rinsed of mud and quickly put into Part 2. If there are enough helpers, some of them can be used to take these fish away from Part 2 as they accumulate and carry them to the transport lorries, or to some holding ponds. (It is obvious that vehicles should be able to come as close as possible to the outlet fish trap. When the lake is being constructed, it is sensible to allow for the building of some sort of road. Perhaps your dam will have been made wide enough so that lorries can drive on it. We woke up to the convenience of this idea when we altered the dam of two of our lakes, and now every time we direct a lorry on to that dam we congratulate ourselves on our good sense.)

If there are not enough helpers to shift the fish, the fish have to remain in Part 2 of the trap. If conditions become overcrowded, one or two stop boards will have to be put into the monk to stop the water flowing out. Of course, this stops the fish from coming through as well, so Part 2 of the trap can be cleared and the fish transferred to the lorries or holding ponds. Then the board can be removed from the monk and water and fish start to move again through the pipeline.

If there is one of these traps in a sport fishery, the fishery has another role as a part-time farm. For example, for years the chain of lakes which comprises Two Lakes, have been emptied periodically and all the tench have been sold. As it is a trout fishery, all efforts of management are concentrated on producing the best it can in trout fishing. The tench are a second crop, not interfering with the trout fishery. But every few years, the sale of great numbers of tench has brought in a good sum of money. The tench are of good quality, because through the frequent emptying of the lakes the tench are young fish which have had no time to over-populate and become stunted.

This sort of combined management of a trout fishery with coarse fish farming is workable for a private owner and as well for a fishing club. Even if the club has no profit motive, the profit from the sale of the coarse fish can be used for improving the trout fishery. It can be used for the amenities of the fishery, or for stocking with more and larger trout, or for building, say, a club house.

It is worth while building a fish catching trap. It need not be an elaborate affair: 30 cm or 60 cm high walls, with a base one metre wide; the length of the compartments 1 and 2, two and three metres . . . these measurements would be quite adequate. If compartments 1 and 2 are made long, there is the advantage that you can divide them into different sections with grids or stop boards.

In a Continental coarse fish farm I saw an interesting addition to compartment 2 of the trap. This was rather long and was divided into three, sometimes four sections. The divisions of the sections were grids of differing widths between the bars. All fish from Part 1 of the trap, after being rinsed, were put into A of Part 2. The largest fish were unable to swim through the grid into B. The next size were unable to swim into C and so only the smallest of the fish finished up in D. All the fish thus sort themselves out into different size groups and are not handled in the process. All this is made possible by allowing a rather strong current through the whole of compartment 2 to encourage the fish to swim into the current as they instinctively will. Figure 22 explains in detail.

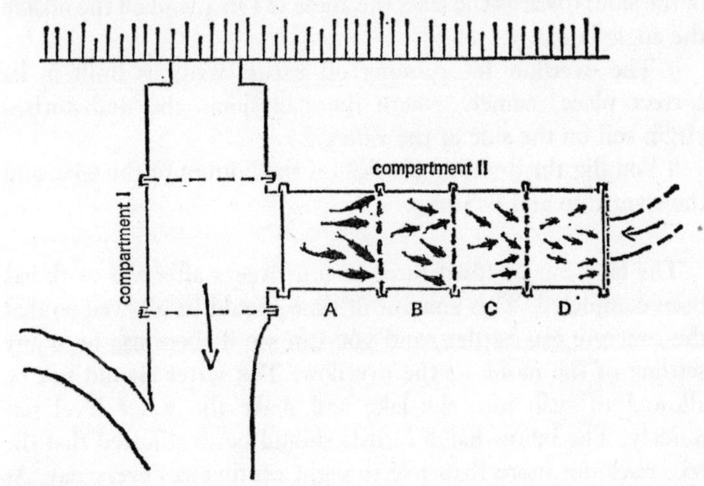

FIGURE 22

It is important that the fresh water should be taken from the stream which flows around the lake. The overflow cannot provide any fresh water because the lake is empty, or at least down to a few centimetres, just sufficient to keep the remaining fish alive. Of course, fresh water can be brought down to compartment 2 of the trap through a hoseline. At Two Lakes, where the trap is not yet installed, there is a tap not too far away and we always have a hose laid on for fresh water when we are emptying a lake. Even without a trap, this fresh water is necessary for the welfare of the fish.

To sum up the various steps in building a lake:

1 You find the correct water level which allows for at least two and a half metres to three metres of depth of water for a trout fishery, or at least one and a half metres depth for a coarse fish fishery.

2 The levels have to be determined so that no neighbouring land is flooded or inconvenienced in any way.

3 You divert the stream in a new stream bed around the lakes.

4 You clear all vegetation away from the ground on which you will build the dam.

5 You lay your pipeline and build your monk.

6 The dam is built, with the greatest attention being given to consolidating the material of the dam and to the correct angle of the side: towards the lake, the angle is 1 in 4, and on the offside the angle is 1 in 3.

7 The overflow for running off excess water is built in its correct place, namely where the dam joins the undisturbed virgin soil on the side of the valley.

8 You dig the draining ditches on the bottom of the lake, add the elver trap and fish trap.

The lake can be filled three to four weeks after the work has been completed. This amount of time should be allowed so that the concrete can harden, and you can see if there has been any settling of the monk or the overflow. The water should not be allowed to rush into the lake and make the water level rise quickly. The inflow hatch boards should be so adjusted that the lake rises not more than five to eight centimetres every day. As the water rises higher and higher, there is great pressure on your various constructions. If the water rises slowly, it enables you to correct anything that may have gone wrong.

What a tremendous satisfaction and feeling of achievement the lake builder feels when, for the first time, he sees his lake full of water. Most of the scars made by the machines are now hidden. Sometimes it takes only a day or two before the first moorhens or duck are seen. The wind makes little ripples, the water is very clear, and it looks nearly perfect. The operative word is 'nearly'. What rather spoils the picture is the rawness of the surroundings. Perhaps the bulldozer had to scrape soil from the hillside, and it shows as a nasty gash, or a road and some houses spoil the scene. And here comes the last job of the planner, the builder, the creator of the new lake: he must shape the surroundings. Some earth moving may be necessary to level minor hills made by the bulldozer, but the work is mostly the planting of trees. Trees form a screen that creates an illusion of solitude and privacy, and that hides ugly buildings and other eyesores. Generally speaking, the screen should be of evergreen conifers – Two Lakes has such a screen, hiding the busy London to Bournemouth road and a number of houses. Of course, all the fishermen know the road is there; some of them have just been on it driving down from London, but the noise of the traffic is to some extent deadened by the trees, and the petrol fumes are surprisingly diminished. As to the nearby houses, some of our fishermen don't even realize that there are any, though in fact, but for the trees, they overlook us. So the fisherman, fishing the quiet lakes with many trees around him, can imagine himself to be deep in the wilderness.

Trees planted for a screen ought to be a reasonable distance away from the banks of the lake. The fly fisherman needs casting space, and the coarse fisherman wants elbow-room. Furthermore, leaf-fall into the lake is diminished if the trees are planted not too close to the banks. When you are making up your mind which trees to plant, your first consideration should be their ability to withstand strong winds. A screen of trees is not often protected by other woodland, and without that protection some species would not last long. The trees should be planted further apart from each other than they would be in forest plantations, say, at least two metres, to make the root growth stronger. Broadleaved trees are not as suitable as conifers, since for many months of the year they have no leaves, and the anglers can still see the intrusive houses, roads, or factories through the skeleton-like branches. However, a few deciduous trees should be planted in every belt of evergreen conifers. A few birches here and there in the first row nearest the lake, give a colourful picture with their very light green in spring, and their red golden leaves in autumn; so does the odd beech, mountain ash, oak, or ornamental cherry. A copper beech breaks the green of the conifers. But all will accord with the personal tastes of the planner.

Different species of conifers have very different greens, from the darkest to the lightest. At Two Lakes there are stretches along the banks of the lakes where Scots Pine, Norway Spruce, Macrocarpa, Douglas Fir and Red Cedar are growing together. They provide an infinite variety of greens and the shapes and textures of the foliage differ too. We planted the odd larch tree among them as well. Though they are not very useful as screens since they lose their needles every autumn, larches enhance the picture: they have the most delicate green in early spring, and are golden in autumn. Japanese Larch are even prettier. At Two

Lakes there are single trees or groups of three or four deciduous trees amongst the conifers. The broadleaved trees are always planted on the inner fringe of the screen, facing the lakes. They need light, and their lower branches would die off if they were crowded too closely by the conifers. Furthermore, most of the conifers will lose their lower branches if they are planted too close together, and in time the screen effect is diminished.

For example, say your screen is five rows deep. Some species with very full foliage (very well furnished as foresters say), should be planted on the outside of the screen facing your neighbour's land: Lawson's Cypress (*Cupressus Lawsoniana*) is an ideal tree; Western Red Cedar (*Thuya plicata*) is a close second, and is very wind firm. Many people have a great affection for the large-coned Cypress (*Cupressus macrocarpa*), as it is very fast growing, and makes an excellent screen. But in certain localities where late and hard frosts occur, it can be killed off suddenly, leaving a troublesome gap

Western Hemlock (*Tsuga heterophylla*) provides a good screen effect, grows very quickly, and is a most beautiful tree with its slender drooping branches. Norway Spruce (*Picea Abies*) is shallow rooted and when planted amongst other trees it is not very wind firm. But if it is planted as a very small tree, maybe three or four years old, on the outside of a screen of trees, the roots develop strongly and the tree withstands strong winds. The same applies to Douglas Fir (*Pseudotsuga taxifolia*). The Scots pine (*Pinus sylvestris*) loses some of its lower branches when it is planted amongst other trees, but not if it is planted on the outer line of the tree screen.

Every screen should have a few Redwoods. There are two varieties: Wellingtonia (*Sequoia wellingtonia*) and Sequoia (*Sequoia sempervirens*). Both come from the West Coast of America, and have been grown in many parts of Europe from imported seed. At Two Lakes about two hundred 30 cm high Sequoias were planted among other screen trees, and twenty years later some of them were ten or more metres tall.

If you want an even greater variety of trees you should visit a forest nursery. Look at the conifers with thick foliage, and those that are wind firm and frost hardy.

There is a tendency to plant willows, alders and poplars near water. One or two of these three may help to beautify the lake, but don't plant too many, as they throw a heavy leaf fall into the water during the autumn.

Shrubs are not quite tall enough for a screen, but a few flowering shrubs are always attractive; though it is important not to make the whole scenery around the lakes look too like a park. Anglers living in cities have plenty of well kept parks that they can walk around to admire the shrubs and flowers. A fishery should be as much as possible a keepered wilderness. At Two Lakes a tree blown down by the wind has been left lying on the ground; one or two trees had their tops broken off by gales, years ago, but the remaining trunks have not been cut down. They look wild, and, more important, they provide nesting places for birds. Nevertheless, with all the wilderness, the management sees to it that the fisherman can walk through the trees alongside the lakes without his rod top being caught up in the branches of the trees. The paths are dry and level, bridges are safe, and seats and rain shelters are provided. Consequently, although the place looks wild and in a state of nature, the anglers are comfortable. Paying attention to these details adds to the enjoyment of a day's fishing.

Once the lake is built, whether it is a private or a club fishery, everybody looks forward with great excitement to the moment when the first fish are introduced. One of the following chapters will deal with stocking of trout and coarse fish fisheries, but first, you should really get clear in your mind what rules you will set to control the fishing season by season, and preserve it for the future.

4 The Rules

Wherever a group of people live, work, or even play together, a certain code of behaviour must be established. The wildest savages have very strict tribal laws, and anyone who breaks those laws is dealt with very effectively, with the result that all the members of the tribe live well organized lives within the recognized boundaries of their discipline. A good fishing club is fundamentally a hunting group, and the stricter the rules, the better the fishing. I'm not suggesting that members who break a rule should have a hand chopped off or be buried in an ant-hill or have the bone pointed at them, but the possibility of expulsion from the hunting group can act as a useful deterrent.

After having spent my young years in fish farming and producing fish for the table market, I switched to the management of an angling water. It was a revelation. I had always understood that fishermen are a special breed of human: honest, law-abiding, peace-loving, helpful, generous minded, self-critical, unselfish, modest and kind. Then I had to deal with them and found that they are just like everyone else – some good, some not so good. Some of them are not in the least ashamed of cheating if the opportunity arises. What can you think when you find *a tin of maggots* underneath the seat of a boat in a trout fishery with the rule 'fly only'? Or when you see a man casting, and with every cast the sunlight catches the brilliant flash of a fly spoon? Then there is the fellow who sneaks to his car before he comes to weigh in with his fish. Should you or your keeper suddenly appear beside him and look into his creel to admire his catch, you would find that the chap could not count to five, the correct bag limit. There are seven trout in his creel, two of which were to be hidden in the boot of his car. Some day someone will write a book about the misdeeds of fishermen, a very long and highly entertaining book.

Deep down, many anglers suspect that the rules of their club or of their fishery have been set up only to annoy them. Almost daily, any keeper or fishery manager has to remind somebody about the rules. Some fishermen, often those of the highest moral rectitude, who would never dream of breaking or bending the law of the land, do not hesitate to misunderstand a fishing rule which has been long established in their club. The familiar explanation is, 'Oh, I thought it meant . . .' and some fantastic nonsense follows.

It is the duty of a fishery manager to explain to the anglers that the regulations are there to protect the fishery, which in the end makes for better fishing. The fishing rules are not an irritant, but are very necessary for the smooth running of the fishery. They must never be broken to suit the convenience of only one member, or to suit the convenience of the fishery manager. Rules must be kept by the members, and they must be kept by the management as well. Always. And the management must have no favourites, and the members must know that there are no favourites.

Furthermore, it is the duty of the fishery manager, over a period of time, to explain each rule to each member, in detail. You will be astonished what a difference it makes if the anglers have had some discussion of this sort and have really understood what you had to say.

At many of the Two Lakes Fishery Management Training Courses rules are discussed by fishery managers. Often the consensus is that all fisheries should have the same regulations, with slight variations to suit special local conditions. Regulations can never remain unaltered for years on end; conditions in the fishery itself, and outside influences too, force a change. As an example, at Two Lakes there was a five fish bag-limit for many years; recently, however, the price of trout and the running expenses rose so fast that the subscriptions were no longer adequate, and the way we found to avoid raising them (always an unpopular move) was to reduce the bag limit from five to four trout. This illustrates that the rules should be flexible, except for some basic principles which provide a guideline. These we will discuss one by one.

1. The Fishing Season opens on 1st April and closes on 30th September.

This cannot be altered by club or fishery owner, the dates are laid down by the Authorities, and vary slightly according to the part of the country. The dates are set so as to give the trout a chance to carry out their spawning activities in peace and quiet.

But, you know, it isn't only the fish that need a close season, keepers and fishery managers and the fishery as well all need a rest. If you have to deal with anglers every day of the week, and I mean all seven days of the week, it can be quite a strain. Then too there are the endless jobs in a fishery that can be done only when no fishing is going on. In a well-run fishery, there is so much to be done that the months of the close season, (when most staff holidays are taken), go by faster than the months of the fishing season.

There are movements afoot to permit year-round fishing for some freshwater fish; and for put and take trout fisheries where the trout do not spawn naturally. But, even without considering the fish or the staff, there is still one considerable argument against an open season, and that is the psychological effect on the fishermen. If the anglers can fish for trout all the year round, the excitement of the sport is diminished. There is no period when fishing is unobtainable; there is no opening day to look forward to. I have talked to a great number of anglers about this, and only a very few have said that they would want to fish all the year around. These are the greedy ones, the pot-hunters who want to fill their deep-freezes with fish and to boast of the great number of trout they have killed. Killed, rather than caught. They are like the white buffalo hunters in America in the 1870s, who killed the buffalo to near-extinction. A food source that the Red Indian had managed instinctively for centuries, was destroyed in a decade by a few greedy men. Some of these buffalo hunters wrote memoirs, and nearly all said that the hunting was fun in the beginning, then it became a business, and finally they found the slaughter sickening. Thanks to the close season our latter day buffalo hunters have not yet reached stage three, through lack of opportunity. But in all fairness, it must be pointed out that there are the buffalo-hunter type of fishery managers who, when a loophole has been found in the law, extend their fishing season merely to make extra money.

Thus, for the fish, for the fishery, for the staff, and for the fishermen's pleasure, it would appear that a close season is in the best interests of the sport.

2. *Rents are payable in the January previous to the fishing season. Payment of rent is considered an acknowledgement of the rules and rent, once paid, is not returnable. Only on payment is a rod considered booked. Every rod fishing at Two Lakes will be furnished with a copy of these regulations and will be required to sign a further copy to be handed to the owner.*

I have pointed out already that fishermen are human and commit many minor sins, and have human failings. Nobody likes paying for what they get, and for that matter no living creature likes paying for what it gets. Something for nothing is wonderful.

When I drafted the rules for the first season at Two Lakes, I settled on April 1st for the date of payment for the rod. The fishing season started on April 1st, so why should anglers pay before that date? In my experience with fish for the table market, I only got paid on delivery, which was businesslike and everyone was happy. So, April 1st dawned, an angler arrived, gave me his cheque, went fishing and caught fish. We were both happy. The next fisherman, to his astonishment, found that he had forgotten his cheque book. There was a little pause; then it was decided that gentlemen are gentlemen and fishermen are gentlemen. He went fishing, caught fish and was very happy but oddly enough he had forgotten his cheque book *again* when he came for his next day's fishing. Oh yes, he paid up, but it was all very embarrassing.

Another angler did not turn up at all, so after a couple of weeks I wrote asking if he was all right, and requesting his subscription. He replied that he did not want his rod after all because he had found fishing much nearer his home. At least he replied to my letter, which was a moderate courtesy. Many people don't even bother to reply. The sad thing is that trout had been bought, all other expenses had been paid, and I was out of pocket because it was too late to attempt to let these rods to someone else.

So I brought the date for the payment of the subscription forward to January 1st. If somebody did not pay by then, I would wait until February 1st. If then, even after a reminder, the money was not forthcoming, I could advertise and find a replacement before the fishing season started. This proved to be a good move and the rods and the payment situation improved, though a few clever dicks still caught me out. I wrote in December asking for the subscription by January 1st, as specified in the rules and as understood and acknowledged. At the end of January the clever dick would write and ask if I would be so understanding as to make an exception and wait a week or so: he was expecting money from somebody and was a bit pressed, but he would pay at once when he got his remittance. It seemed a reasonable request, and he seemed sincere in his assurances that he was not cancelling his booking. I did not bother to advertise for a replacement. And I never heard another word from him!

It was obvious that the most satisfactory date for collecting the subscriptions was not January 1st, so I took the step which I should have taken at the very beginning – I wrote to several long-established and thriving angling clubs and private fisheries and asked for their rules. They all specified that at the end of a fishing season the rods were expected to pay their subscriptions in advance for the coming season. So, accordingly, as fishing at Two Lakes finished on the last day of September, payment of subscriptions for the following season could be expected in October. It seemed to me a very attractive proposition indeed, and if such old and famous clubs could establish such a rule, why not Two Lakes? But I feared I would never get away with it.

The rules of Two Lakes were altered accordingly, and payment for the next year's subscription is now required in October. Some fishermen agreed without a murmur, but most wanted to know why the payment had to be so early. Prefacing my explanation by pointing out that I was following the lead of other fisheries, I answered that I had to know well before the fishing season commenced exactly how many rods would be fishing, and further, if a subscription had not been paid I had no guarantee that the rod would not let me down. The third reason I gave made the fishermen happy about paying in October. If I had all the subscriptions safely in the kitty, I could order all the trout that the fishery needed; I would not have to cancel my order and I could pay the fish farmer immediately on delivery of the fish. If a trout farmer knows that his customer will not cancel even part of his order, and will pay on delivery, he will look after that

above The collapsed side at the back of the dam. The sides are too steep and the water on the lake side seeped through at too high a level.

right When cracks appear in a dam it must be rebuilt.

left An overflow under construction. As a safeguard the width of the overflow must never be underestimated.

below The elver trap. In the small gap between the two brick walls, on the right, there is the pipe, spouting water, to entice the elvers to enter the trap.

customer's interests. The fishery will benefit, and the angler will know that the trout are there for him to catch.

For years, now, the subscriptions at Two Lakes are collected in October and all members have become used to it. When vacancies occur and new members are taken on, they see that everybody else pays in October, and they conform. And the members know that if they do not pay their subscriptions in time, there is somebody else waiting to step into their shoes.

It is an important addition to the rule that subscriptions once paid will not be refunded. A club with a reasonable number of members will find that every year one or two members will ask for their money back. This presents management with a problem identical to the one which arises when subscriptions are not paid for rods which have been booked. If money is refunded there is that much less with which to pay for the stock fish which have been ordered already, or for improvements which have been planned and perhaps already begun. It is detrimental to the fishery, and unfair to the other members. The reasons given for the request for a refund may be plausible, but in most cases the real reason is that the member wants to go to another fishery where he thinks he will get better sport.

A solution to the problem is to allow anyone wishing to cancel his subscription to find a replacement rod who is acceptable to the club. This applies even in the case of a man dying before the fishing season commences: the widow must be responsible though an exception could be made, were she to find herself in severely reduced circumstances – an unlikely event as a man who can afford to fish is not exactly a pauper.

More than once in our salad days we were faced with this problem of a death before the opening of the season. One instance was particularly hard for us to swallow: the couple were very well heeled, and the husband was an invalid. We had bought a boat to make fishing easier for him, and were dismayed when, shortly before the opening day, we had a letter from the wife to inform us that her husband was seriously ill and in hospital. Before we had time to reply, there was a further letter with 'grave news' (after all these years I still remember that well-chosen phrase) and in the afternoon post of the same day there was another and most distraught bulletin. By this time we were feeling terribly guilty that we hadn't responded sooner to such heart-breaking cries for sympathy, and hastened to write a very diplomatic letter expressing our deepest compassion, and enclosing a cheque which we hoped wasn't tactless of us considering the infinitely distressing circumstances. We never heard another word from her, and subsequently we learned from another source that a few months later the unhappy woman's husband did die. We were stuck with the boat because it wasn't suitable for the working of the fishery, and normally we allowed no boat fishing.

Often, members will try to get out of an argument over the rules by saying that they are unaware of such and such a rule. It is advisable to have each member sign a copy of the rules and to keep these signed copies safely for they can be used to settle arguments, and as a means of enforcing the rules. A fishery manager must never forget that running an angling water is like being in charge of a business venture. You will have to deal with all sorts of people and disentangle many problems. Signed contracts are a basis for security. Signed copies of the rules are your contracts.

3. No River Board Licence is necessary, as Two Lakes holds a General Licence.

Everybody who fishes for trout or salmon must have a licence from the Water Authority, and in some areas everybody who fishes for coarse fish must have a licence too. Such a licence can be for one day, one week, one month, or for the whole season of a particular year. It can be bought by the angler himself, or the fishery can hold a General Licence, covering anybody fishing in their waters. A fishery owned by a club or by a private individual must apply to the Water Authority for such a General Licence. If it is granted, the cost of such a licence depends on the size of the fishery and on how many anglers fish it. The price of such a licence adds to the cost of running a fishery and must be passed on to the anglers. The advantage of a General Licence to the man in charge of the fishery is that he need not run after every fisherman to check if he has a licence; and the advantage to the anglers is that they don't have to bother with obtaining one. To avoid any misunderstanding, the angler must have this licence *as well as* permission from the club or private owner to fish. Sometimes a stranger may appear on your fishery, all innocent and beguiling, and insist that his game fishing licence entitles him to fish your waters free of charge. We have had just that happen here at Two Lakes.

The managers of many fisheries prefer not to take out a General Licence, but instead come to an arrangement with the Water Authorities whereby they are allowed to sell licences direct to anglers on their behalf. If the fishery is so large that there is an office, it will make only a little extra work for the staff.

The management must decide what is more advantageous to them. It would not be easy to estimate the amount of a General Licence in fisheries selling many day-tickets, in view of the fact that the management of a day-ticket water can never be sure of how many anglers will be fishing on any particular day. If there is a prolonged period of rain and strong winds, then there will only be the odd fisherman braving the elements; on the other hand, if there is fine weather during the holiday season, the water is crowded. Obviously, on this sort of day-ticket water, selling licences daily to anglers would be more convenient, whereas a season-ticket water with a set number of fishermen is better off with a General Licence.

4. Dry Fly Fishing only is permitted to the 1st of July, and from then onwards to the end of the season a wet fly also is allowed. Only one fly must be attached to the cast.

This rule has subsequently been altered to 'Fly fishing only is permitted. Only one Fly must be attached to the cast. No hook larger than 2 cm.' This rule can be better understood by the fishery manager who is an angler himself, or is at least knowledgeable about fly fishing. As I have said before many of the best fishery managers I know, both here and abroad, are non-anglers, but they know everything there is to know about tackle and the catching of fish, about artificial flies, natural flies and the various creepy-crawlies.

I am a non-angler. The more involved I became with fishery management, the less I bothered with actual fishing, until I gave it up completely. But anything to do with angling is of the deepest and most absorbing interest to me.

When I launched Two Lakes as a fly-only fishery, I had to choose whether we would allow any fly-like imitation, or would be purists: dry-fly only. Now, Two Lakes is situated between two world famous dry-fly fishing rivers, the Test and the Itchen – in fact, the overflow stream from Two Lakes is a tributary of the River Test and joins the river near Romsey. In such a distinguished neighbourhood we felt that we ought to permit only dry-fly, but lake fishing at that time was not quite fashionable, and besides, Two Lakes was without the very heavy fly hatches of a chalk stream, so I compromised, and ruled that from July 1st and onwards, wet-fly would be allowed. This rule stood for a few years, but gradually I realized that it was not very fair to the anglers. Many of them had to travel several hours by car to fish at Two Lakes and after a day's fishing, they had the same long drive home. To travel that distance and to find on arrival that dry-fly fishing was out because there was no fly hatch, and then to travel that tiring distance back with no fish because no other methods were allowed, seemed a little hard. The purist ideal is compatible with bygone days when the pace of life was more leisurely. Nowadays there is less time to spare and the fisherman needs true relaxation in his brief time off. He wants to cast, to hook a fish, to play it, to land it and take it home, and to tell his family all the details of the catch (insisting it was caught on a dry-fly), and in the end to eat it. Not for him the esoteric approach of the dry-fly purist . . . *in practice*.

So the rule at Two Lakes was altered, and wet flies and nymph fishing were allowed. We have found the arrangement highly satisfactory. Many of our rods fish exclusively with a dry-fly, and when there are good hatches of olives, they catch their limit more quickly than do the other rods.

One point must be taken into consideration when rules are being drawn up for a new fishery, and that is its locality. Certain parts of the country provide certain types of sport and this will influence the rules.

Rule number 4 further states that only one fly must be attached to the cast. In a water holding small trout, where a pounder is a monster, it may be quite in order to fish with three flies. If it should happen that you hook and then play two or three trout at the same time, it is quite possible to land all of them. Anglers tell long and exciting stories of such tussles, and let it be known how clever they were to land more than one trout at a time. Very few anglers admit that one or two fish are often lost on such an occasion, or give a thought to what happens to the trout subsequently. Even if we are so heartless as to care little about the fate of the trout, in a heavily fished water where economic considerations are important, a dead or injured or ailing trout counts as a financial loss. In a water holding large trout it is lunacy to allow more than one fly on the cast. Of course anglers want to increase their chances of catching fish, and of course three hooks are better than one for increasing those chances; but equally the chances of fish being lost are increased and the damage to the quality of fishing is also increased. The most valuable trout in a fishery is a trout which has been hooked by an angler, played by him, landed by him, and taken home by him, and the management must do its utmost to prevent that valuable fish from becoming an unsavoury corpse, floating around in the water, white tummy upwards, announcing to the world that it is dead.

The addition I have made to rule 4 limits the size of the hook, and in this I have again followed the example of many other fisheries, club and private. There are many and varying reasons for this rule. A large hook is likely to be more injurious to a fish that is lost. Many people hold that a few feathers tied to a large hook do not constitute an artificial fly in the proper meaning of the term. Many people hold, and here I agree with them, that to drag through the water a large hook with a few feathers tied to it is 'feathered spinning' and not fly fishing; even small hooks with long shanks are not representative of natural flies but of little fish. With these last allegations, the fishery manager is in a difficult position, and it is as well to adjust his policy to the strength of his position. If he owns the fishery, or is in unquestioned control, he can lay down the law and brook no arguments. But if there is a committee to consider, there may have to be some compromise. Fishermen have their likes and dislikes and the committee members are fishermen; they view the running of their club from the fisherman's point of view. The manager must point out that the welfare of the angling water itself is of prime importance, closely followed by the reputation of the fishery. It cannot be designated as a Fly Fishing Water if the rules are so loosely constructed that all sorts of contraptions (including day old chicks on meat hooks) can be used as flies.

As time passes, so outlooks and demands alter. At one of our Fishery Management Training Courses here at Two Lakes, a frank statement was made by a cheerful young man, a statement that impressed me very much indeed: 'If I go fishing for trout I try first with a dry-fly. I think that is the best fun, but if the conditions are hopeless, I try with a wet-fly. If I still cannot catch any trout, I start spinning.' There's a nice little problem, and what's more, the fishery managers will have to sort it out!

5. *Rods are not entitled to more than one visit per week. A day or part thereof is counted as one visit. Each rod is booked for a particular day of the week, and any alteration must be by arrangement with the owner.*

When you open a fishery, you must make the decision whether the fishery becomes a season-ticket water or a day-ticket water. Very seldom can day-tickets and season-tickets be worked together on the same water to everybody's satisfaction. Sooner or later the day-ticket holder complains about the special rights the season-ticket holder has, and vice versa. Even when a manager has done his utmost to be fair to both parties, the anglers will not agree. Then there is the problem of the price of the tickets. Often the price of a day-ticket is not commensurate with the price of the season-ticket on the same water. A very well-known day-ticket water comes to mind on this score. It carries as well a few season-tickets which cost £40. The day-ticket costs £1 and the season extends to twenty-five weeks, so if a season-ticket angler fishes one day a week, he could have had his season's fishing for £25. Indeed, should he have fished two days a week, he would only have paid £50. The only advantage to the season-ticket holder, it would appear, is that he doesn't have to waste valuable time in going and buying a ticket each time he fishes.

Although I gather from information collected from many season-ticket waters that quite a number of ticket holders do not fish every week, there are exceptions. I know of one angler living only a few minutes' walk away from a reservoir where he has a season ticket, and where he fishes *every day*, and has done for years. This is such a notable exception that it is worth mentioning. Decidedly it demonstrates the wisdom of limiting visits to one day a week.

Likewise, to help in the efficient running of a smaller fishery season-ticket holders cannot be allowed to come on any day they choose. Should the rules allow this, too many members might appear on the same day and the water would be disagreeably crowded. Then there would be the inevitable complaints. The only solution would be to have only as many members as could be accommodated on one day without overcrowding, but this would mean paying an unusually heavy subscription. So you introduce a rule that each member must choose a day of the week and stick to his choice. Because the management knows exactly how many members fish each day and how many fishermen the water can take, there is no risk in increasing the daily number of rods to the optimum and suddenly the fishery has more paying anglers, which is reflected in the income of the fishery. Of course, the expenditure on stocking will be higher, but the profits are in proportion. Even a club run on non-profit making lines surely will not object to having some surplus cash. There are many things on which such a surplus could be spent with benefit to every member of the club.

There are many angling clubs, not only in this country, who reject these premises. They take a different approach. Their first consideration is the cheapness of the fishing, and the members are left to roam at will, with as few rules as possible. These ideas have always interested me, because they sound ideal, and a fishery where they were followed through successfully would be a nirvana for fishermen. The trouble is that when the managements of these clubs are investigated, it is found that invariably they have two features in common. First, they have a very quick turnover of members: most fishermen leave after one or two seasons, and often the club is rather short of members. Secondly their finances are in a very bad state.

Anglers, like most people, dislike muddle. They prefer the firm but fair rules which are necessary for the provision of good sport. They are quite prepared to pay for what they get (if there is no possible way of getting their fishing free); club or private fishery, game or coarse fishery, the same criteria apply.

6. *All rods and their guests fishing at Two Lakes, or visiting at Two Lakes, do so entirely at their own risk, and the owner takes no responsibility for any damage, accident, or injury of whatsoever kind or nature which may result, or for loss of or damage to their property.*

You must not think that this clause means that you will not be held responsible for any accident to the anglers or their guests: you *must* have an All Risks Insurance policy.

For the careless, a fishery can be a dangerous place. A fast river or a deep lake can be a death-trap and if boats and bridges are not in good repair they can cause serious trouble. Banks are often slippery and it is easy to lose one's foothold and fall and break a limb. Moreover, we mustn't overlook what pike's teeth, hooks, and other sharp things can do to the fishermen who are very quick to blame the management for everything. Management is the whipping-boy for bad weather, for trout not rising, for carp not taking the bait, for fish not fighting well, for fish being lost, so why should it not be the management's fault too if a hook gets stuck in a fisherman's finger, or even worse, in his face? The car park may be large and well laid out, but at some times there are more cars than at other times and if they bump into one another, management is blamed. People are very careless with their possessions, and if something appears to be lost, theft is suggested at once and often the management is the first suspect. And so it goes on.

So, have your bridges and boats in reasonable repair, put gravel where the ground is slippery and mark places that might be hazardous; in other words, take reasonable precautions. You can also try warning the fishermen of any dangers, and hope that this will encourage them to be careful. Your rules will make your position clear regarding the various mishaps which are purely the fisherman's fault and if law suits are threatened, let the insurance company fight it out.

7. *No responsibility is taken for any disaster that may happen to the lakes or the trout, viz.: flood, drought, disease, etc., whereby fishing is rendered impossible.*

If the fisherman spends his holiday in a fishing hotel and has the bad luck to strike a period when the rivers are low, the salmon remain in the estuary, there is no prospect of rain and little hope of a run, he will suffer agonies of frustration; but he has no idea of what the hotel management is going through. About ninety-nine per cent of the anglers will blame the management, and some will even demand their money back. The wretched man who runs the hotel would be more than delighted if every guest were to catch several salmon, for satisfied customers mean heavy bookings for the next season. But the frustrated fisherman can think of nothing but his own disappointment and when he joins a syndicate or club, his behaviour isn't any different; he will hold the management responsible for his frustration. If the management has a rule such as rule 7, they have something to turn to when the going gets very rough though there are certain preventive measures they should have taken before doing so.

For instance, in man-made fisheries, such as small artificial lakes, there is less danger of flood if the feeder stream does not flow direct into the lake, or if there is a large overflow and a sensible monk to cope with surplus water. Moreover, the danger of drought can be lessened by making your lake deeper than is actually necessary, so that it can afford to lose a foot or two during a rainless period. A prudent management will also take every precaution to avoid disease, but even in the best regulated fisheries diseases can strike quite ruthlessly, and fishing be curtailed. In such circumstances, the manager or owner of the fishery needs rule 7 as a shield against the anger of the members, who sometimes seem uncomprehending in their demands. Unfortunately there is nothing to protect him against the damage such a calamity will do to the reputation of the fishery.

8. All fish caught must be recorded for the purpose of keeping a log book.

As I have said several times already, a sport fishery is a business and it must be run in an efficient and business-like way. Even an angling club run on non-profit-making lines must have some structure and system of management. Records must be kept of the fish stocked and the fish caught, of the club's finances, of membership and of the physical conditions and changes in the fishing waters, as discussed in Chapter 1. The owner of a private fishery must be even more careful to keep accurate and extensive records.

It is a constant source of amazement to me to hear of the many clubs and private owners of fisheries who do not bother to keep an accurate log-book. Generally there is no log-book because it is too much trouble for both the management and the fishermen. I can only say that they deserve each other! The log-book for the accurate notation of all catches is an absolute necessity if only because: first, statistics of catches are needed for short-term management and for long-term management; second, if the fishery should ever have to be sold, the value of the fishery will depend to a very great degree on the catches of the previous years (and in some cases the value of the fishery will depend *entirely* on these catches). Only proper recorded catches will be acceptable evidence.

For most fishery managers, paper work is a misery and a burden and as most fisheries are not large enough to employ permanent secretarial staff, keeping the log-book is a job that the manager cannot delegate. But it is important. He must do the job himself and he must make the entries daily.

Who weighs the fish is a matter of convenience. At Two Lakes all trout are brought to the house, and the fish are put on the balance and weighed in the angler's presence. The figures are written down on a daily catch sheet, and the weights are also written on a separate sheet of paper for the angler. The next day all the weights on the catch sheets are entered into the log-book, that is to say the weight of each individual trout and the total weight of each bag. This means extra work but is a valuable means of settling arguments at a later stage, and prevents any disappointed anglers from accusing Two Lakes of fiddling the books. I keep the daily catch sheets until the end of each season. Every angler knows that he can inspect the log-book at any time, so long as his hands are clean!

Many fisheries prefer the anglers to fill out prepared cards and after every visit to the fishery to send these cards back to the management with all the data. Other fisheries are satisfied with a record of total catch for the season, sent in by the fishermen at the end of the season. As you may have guessed, I don't think much of this arrangement. I don't see how it can produce accurate records. Anglers are lax about sending off cards with their returns, especially when the returns are nil. Quite a long time after the fishing season is over there are notices from well-known fisheries in the angling press asking fishermen please to send in their returns. It is very difficult to plan for the coming season when only a certain number of fishermen have sent in their records. Much of the preparation of the figures for future stocking is left to guess-work and the sad thing is that when fisheries' final catches are reported in the fishing press, there is an angry cry of 'guess-work!' from those very fishermen who couldn't be bothered to send in their returns when they were due!

	Visits
	Date
	Name
	Naboth's Lake
	Spring
	Border
	Upper Lake
	Lower Lake
	Chalky
	Home Pool
	Total number of trout caught
	Fly
	Fish weights
	Total weight
	Remarks

FIGURE 23

Now, not for one moment would I contend that the log-book we have at Two Lakes must be taken as a model, as log-books, like rules, must suit local conditions. Be that as it may, I have tried to limit the headings to cover the essential facts. (See Figure 23 for facsimile of page of log-book.) The first column is the number of the angler's visit and as a fisherman's memory can be very vague when it suits him it's as well to make a careful note here so there can be no subsequent arguments. When you enter the fisherman's name, see to it that the spelling is correct, and that you have the initials right. This information is essential when catches are reported in the angling press for when a fisherman makes an outstanding catch, he wants to be sure that his friends know about it! Over the years a good number of letters have arrived from all over the globe, from people who saw the name of a long lost friend mentioned in the Two Lakes fishing reports. It has always been the greatest pleasure to pass these letters on. And while we are on the subject of the correct spelling of the name and the correct initials, the fishery manager who cannot be bothered with this sort of accuracy is both bad mannered and stupid.

It is worth while, when a fishery consists of different lakes or several beats on a river, that the fish from each lake or river beat is recorded separately. If this is done carefully, especially in put-and-take fisheries, the management knows at any time how many fish are in a given piece of water. This is a great help in any restocking programme.

The next column in our log-book is for specifying what fly or flies the angler used. Years ago, when the number of artificial flies numbered a few hundred, and when most anglers fished with the more traditional patterns, it was helpful if the flies used were noted in order to determine which were the most successful artificials. As the interest in fly-fishing increased, so did the interest in fly-tying, and not only the professional fly-tyers, but also the countless amateur fly-tyers, began to invent numerous new patterns. Nowadays, nearly everybody uses his own patterns, or the one given most recent publicity in the sporting press, and this is particularly true in put and take fisheries where the hatch of natural flies is often ignored. Quite frequently, after a day's fishing, the log-book indicates that each angler caught his fish on a different fly. This variety in fishing methods has spread from the reservoirs to most rivers, with the possible exception of some of the chalk streams. Consequently, it is questionable if it is any longer of value to record the fly used in the log-book. Since history tends to repeat itself, however, we will discuss, in a later chapter, the possibility that there may be a revival of traditional fly-fishing.

In our progress from column to column, we now come to the recording of the fish's weight. Here again accuracy is essential. In a fishery where the stock fish are small and are given time to grow on, such records are an indication of the well-being of the fish. In a fishery where the stock fish are introduced when they are of catchable size, the records give a good idea of whether or not the trout are of the size that were ordered from the trout farm, and whether or not it is worth while to stock with large fish. In some waters fish lose weight quickly and if they are not caught soon they will become thin and ugly-looking, and will be a great disappointment to the angler. On these fisheries, if the manager has the records of the weights of the fish, he will know that something is amiss and can decide what action he should take in order to put things right. He may have to stock with smaller fish or to improve the natural food supply; or, where it is possible from a practical point of view, and the expense can be justified, he may decide to feed the fish artificially.

The final column in the Two Lakes log-book is for 'remarks'. Should a club or a private fishery have, for argument's sake, fifty members, the fishery manager will find to his great astonishment that he has forty-five colleagues. The remaining five members will never pretend that they are anything more than just ordinary anglers, but the rest will always be prepared to advise and criticize, grumble and interfere with the management. No fishery manager should be so conceited that he thinks he is above criticism, constructive criticism, that is, not frivolous or carping complaints. To provide a member with the opportunity to air his grievances, give him a little space in the log-book. He is reluctant to put anything too silly in writing, if only because his fellow members will see it.

Ideally, every day's entry in the log-book should be signed by the angler, however, in practice, this isn't possible, since when the weigh-in takes place, the fisherman's hands are often too wet and dirty to touch a book which is meant to last for years and eventually be handed down to the next generation. If the management is determined to have each angler's signature and if the fishery is not a one-man-band like Two Lakes, there is a sensible method I saw used on some Continental angling waters. The bailiff had a small book, rather like a receipt book, and when all the particulars of a catch were written down, the angler had to sign this and was given a carbon copy. The following day all the entries in the receipt book were copied in the log-book proper by the office staff. The receipt book was kept, very sensibly, for several years in case there should be any queries.

A log-book should be as simple as possible and easy to keep up. In fisheries stocked with fry or yearlings, which attain catchable size after three or four years, the log-book will have to be much more informative than that at Two Lakes. Figure 24 reproduces the headings in the catch books of some Eastern European fisheries. At first glance, the number of columns is rather daunting but the data, in the hands of experts, is certainly worth having.

9. *Every Trout caught must be killed, irrespective of size or condition. Bag limit is two and a half brace per rod per day. Only Trout from a pound in weight upwards are counted. Smaller Trout can be kept without being entered into the log-book or being counted as part of the bag, but rods are asked not to fish deliberately for undersized fish. When five fish over one pound each in weight have been caught, fishing must stop.*

This rule touches on a very delicate subject for anglers. Nearly every fisherman dislikes killing small fish – fish which are under the size limit, and for many years it was the accepted practice to return these fish to the water – an act which made anglers feel very saintly and sporting. The expression 'To throw a small fish back' was used for many years, and then as anglers became conservation-conscious, the wording changed to 'to put an undersized fish back'. The best way to return a fish to the water is to slide your fingers down the cast, get hold of the shank of the hook, hold it firmly under water and let the fish struggle free; many a fish can regain its lost freedom with such help. But a really well-hooked fish cannot. It must be taken out of the water in a net, and held while being unhooked. However, the human hand

	1	Date	
	2	Barometer rdg morning	
	3	Barometer rdg evening	
	4	Temperature morning	
	5	Temperature evening	
	6	Wind	
	7	Weather	
	8	Fishing time from to	
	9	Particulars of river or lake fished	
	10	Methods used. Spinning, bait, fly	
	11	Brown trout	F · I · S · H
	12	Rainbow trout	
	13	Pike	
	14	Catfish	
	15	Zander	
	16	Perch	
	17	Carp	
	18	Tench	
	19	Roach	
	20	Rudd	
	21	Barbel	
	22	Bream	
	23	Chub	
	24	Eel	
	25		
	26		
	27		
	28		
	29	Length of fish	
	30	Weight	
	31	Remarks	
	32	Name	

FIGURE 24

is liable to disturb the fish's protective slime and even a wet hand or cloth will do this and may also damage the scales. Additionally, there is the possibility that the grip of the human hand, however slight, may cause the fish internal injury.

But how much damage is done to the fish? In angling circles it was assumed that every returned *but injured* fish would die sooner or later from some disease or other. In the angling press of many countries heated arguments went on, but nobody could offer proof to back their theories. Then two instances were reported. Research workers in Canada and in New Zealand, independently and unknown to each other, carried out the following experiment: A small carrier stream flowing parallel with the main river but only a few yards away from it was selected, and this little stream was fenced off for a mile or so upstream and downstream. None of the undersized trout caught in the main river were returned, but instead were put into the enclosed side stream after being unhooked with the greatest possible care. After many months, in one instance, a year, it was found that very few of the returned trout had died but between eighty to ninety per cent had not grown as had their relatives of the same age group which were caught later in the main river and killed. This eighty to ninety percent of trout were termed, in farming language, 'bad doers'. The conclusion was that only a very small percentage of those fish had *not* been affected by being hooked, played, landed and handled. It certainly makes you think.

There is another point to be considered, one of great importance to the fishery manager. How much does a fish learn when it has been hooked and then released? Does the 'educated' fish become uncatchable?

We come back to what we have learned by experience at Two Lakes. In the first few years of Two Lakes as a rod-letting fishery, all the stocking was carried out before the opening day. Anglers had very good sport for the first month, and then it tapered off and came to a standstill. According to the log-book, only half of the stock fish were caught. Poaching and loss from vermin were not significant, and it was quite obvious to me that the trout were still in the lakes. I could see them. But not the fishermen. They were convinced that the lakes were fished out. After the close of the fishing season, one of the lakes was drained, and all the remaining trout were caught. Their number tallied very closely with what should have been there according to the log-book. For two or three years subsequently the pattern was the same: stocking before the season commenced, good sport for the first month, then a tapering off which finally became a stand-still.

The only answer could be that after the first few weeks of fishing so many trout had been lost after being hooked, or landed and returned, that in time they became gut-shy, and the faintest shadow on the bank drove them off in panic. To confuse the issue, anglers sometimes told me that they hooked and returned the same trout two or three times during one evening's fishing. This trout must have been the village idiot. Another detrimental effect of the shyness in taking an artificial fly, dry, wet or nymph, was that the trout must have been too cautious even to take a natural fly. A live shrimp or a live nymph were suspect as well. The trout caught during the draining operation were in poor condition for the most part, yet there was plenty of food in the lakes, snails, shrimps, water hog louse, nymphs, caddis, the lot.

Unquestionably, the policy of allowing the return to the water of undersized fish together with only one stocking, and that before the season commenced, provided very uneven sport, so the rule was changed to 'Every trout caught must be killed irrespective of size or condition', and the stocking programme was altered from one large pre-season stocking, to two or three during the season. The results were most encouraging.

Sport was more even throughout the season, and the only injured or educated fish were those which were lost. When the lakes were emptied after the close of the season, it was found that of the surviving trout a great number were in good condition and could be used again. The customers too, were well-satisfied, and made this clear by booking ahead for the next season. I would say that credit for the improvement could be apportioned seventy-five per cent to the changed rule concerning the return of trout to the water, and twenty-five per cent to the alteration of the stocking programme.

The return of undersized fish becomes a more difficult problem in a fishery where no sizeable fish are stocked, and sport is provided from small fish grown up to a takeable size. If the rules require that such small fish be killed, there may not be enough fish left to grow on. One possible way out of the difficulty would be that the water should be fished lightly, although this would not be practical on the smaller waters. It would apply best to large expanses, such as reservoirs, where the proportion of fishermen to the number of hectares of water is lower.

10. Permits are not transferable. Rod sharing is permitted, but only one rod may be used at the time and only one rod's limit of fish may be killed by rod and guest together. Further, every season ticket holder can bring four guests without an extra charge, but not more than one guest at a time may be brought. On such a guest ticket, the guest is entitled to the same daily limit as is the season rod. Rods are asked not to bring as their guests fishing novices, and particularly not to bring children.

Angling waters charging a high price for a season ticket, as for example many of those on the River Test, have found, over the years, that few people are prepared to take a full rod; they can seldom afford to. The reaction of the management of these fisheries has been to offer half and quarter tickets. In one instance, a full season ticket costs £700 but as this permits the ticket holder to fish on every day of the week, it is the equivalent of seven one-day-a-week tickets. Sometimes the ticket is broken down even further, so that the fisherman comes one day every fortnight, and I understand that there are other still more complex arrangements. This jigsaw system helps maintain the façade of an expensive and exclusive fishery, and even the man who fishes only one day a fortnight can delude himself into believing in it. He can say quite truthfully, 'I fish a water where the cost of a rod is £700.' Of course, with equal truth he could say, 'For £50 I fish a water where the cost of a rod is £700,' and that will impress the Joneses even more.

Among the lesser breeds of fisheries, it is usual for season tickets to cost about £100 and to entitle the angler to one day's fishing a week, on an agreed day. On the whole, this arrangement is the most satisfactory for both angler and management. Everybody knows where he is, and nobody bothers about appearances. Once again, an example will underline the argument.

At Two Lakes an angler took a season rod which entitled him to fish every Tuesday during the season. He lived near Winchester, close to the river Itchen where he had an expensive season ticket entitling him to fish on any and every day of the week. He had held this right for years, but told me, during the course of a conversation, that he had never fished so much as he had since he took a rod at Two Lakes. Because he could fish only on Tuesdays, he knew that if he missed a Tuesday he would miss his fishing at Two Lakes for that week, so he did his utmost never to let this happen. Rain or shine, he would come. His wife, his friends, the village, everybody knew that on Tuesdays he was out of circulation: gone fishing. But with his river-fishing, things were different. Because the expensive ticket entitled him to fish on any one day, it sometimes happened that he did not fish the river for two or three weeks in succession. His explanation was that if he made up his mind to go down to the river on, say, a Friday, something might happen to delay him, in his profession, or socially, or he might not feel well, or the weather might be shocking. So he decided not to go on the Friday and it didn't matter that much because he knew he could go any time. There was always the probability that he would go the next day or the next, till suddenly he realized that he had not fished the river for a fortnight. There was no urgency, he had no feeling that he was missing out. As a sequel, it is interesting to know that the fishing on the Itchen has since altered its rules to one day a week. If this set day is so satisfactory for the fishery and the angler, why allow that day to be split? Why allow rod sharing?

Anybody opening a season-ticket water will be surprised at the number of people who want to take a ticket and share it with a friend. Now, to the manager who is a novice in fishery management, this suggestion may sound reasonable, and he may be prepared to comply with it. Little does he realize the trouble that is in store for him, and how difficult it will be to break the stranglehold of the split ticket. He will soon find that sharing is a truly wonderful thing. One fisherman pays half the ticket and the other pays the other half. One fishes in the morning, and one fishes in the afternoon; or they come alternating weeks. Some fishermen are very inventive and think up the most outlandish schemes. To the innocent manager it would appear that all is in order so long as the combined catch of the two anglers does not exceed one rod's limit each week. But there are pitfalls. In the first place, the manager has to deal with two people for the price of one ticket. Even one angler takes up a considerable amount of time. He writes letters, he telephones, he wants to talk to you. He brings his wife or his children or friends and they talk to you. It all chips away at the manager's time, but is part of the job. Now, however, with the shared ticket, the angler has suddenly doubled. Two letters, two telephone calls, two conversations, two wives – and all for the price of one! Moreover, if the rod-sharers have a squabble you have a fight on your hands.

The fishery is the loser in this situation. I know. I have dealt with it. We allowed rod sharing during the first years after the opening of Two Lakes and ran through the whole gamut of discordant notes. The climax was when one of two anglers who fished alternating weeks came to me and complained that on his day fishing was almost always impossible. When I looked in the log-book I found that he was right. Heat-waves, thunderstorms, revolutions, all occurred on his day. His partner nearly always had perfect conditions, and caught many fish. All this had nothing to do with me. I didn't cause the thunderstorms and heat-waves, I didn't even start the revolutions, but who can convince a disappointed angler? So, in the end, both men fished every week . . . for the price of one, and I brought in a new rule at the end of that season to make it quite clear that rod-sharing is not permitted. And this is not a rule that I will reconsider although I am sometimes asked to.

There is another ingenious ploy, the secret, or private, rod-sharing. Here, the fisherman has sold part of his ticket behind your back. Nothing definite is said, but the rod holder regularly lets the management know that he will not be fishing and is sending a friend to fish instead. We put an end to this by stipulating that nine times during the season a ticket holder can share his rod with one other person, but they cannot both fish at the same time, and the ticket holder must always be present. He can never send another person instead of himself.

If you look at the advertisements in the sporting press, you will see that none of the best fisheries offer part-time tickets. An offer of short-term tickets means that a fishery cannot let full tickets, and is pretty desperate. If in the first few seasons of a new fishery the manager cannot let the full quota of tickets, he should not be tempted to settle for anything less. If he is patient, and provides good sport, he will find that after a season or two he will attract his full number of rods.

Tickets should not be transferable. This is explained in the discussion of rule 2, so I won't go over it again, except to stress that where this rule is broken the person who takes over the ticket must be subject to the manager's approval, otherwise the fishery could be saddled with an angler who has been barred as a misfit on other fisheries.

Concerning guest tickets, a bad fishery does not tempt the rod holder to bring his friends as guests, but where the fishing is good, he is pleased to be able to share his sport with friends. In the past, Two Lakes allowed each ticket holder to bring four guests during the season, and there was no extra charge, but because of the rising running costs, this privilege has had to be withdrawn, and the season-ticket holder must now pay for his guests. When the new rule was introduced, there were some interesting consequences. The number of guests dropped considerably. Rods thought twice about paying out hard cash, and the fishery benefited from the lessening of fishing pressure, yet suffered no financial loss. Those who came as guests were skilful fishermen who caught fish, and good fish to boot. Furthermore, quite a number of these guests, after a good day's sport, asked to be put on the waiting list.

Previously, with the four free guest tickets, the season-ticket holder felt that he must use them all. Maybe he had one or two friends who were expert fishermen, but for the remaining ticket or tickets he brought any Tom, Dick or Harry, so as not to waste them. Watching the fishing methods of some of these last-minute guests, I could have wept. I asked one of my rods why on earth he had brought a certain fellow who couldn't fish for toffee. The fisherman explained that the man was a neighbour who had pestered him constantly to bring him to Two Lakes. The neighbour had given florid accounts of his own fishing exploits and was very free with all the correct fishing jargon. Naturally my fisherman thought the chap must be a good angler. Because the rules at Two Lakes require rods not to bring novices as their guests, this particular one had misled his host and created an embarrassing situation. The free tickets, moreover, acted as a magnet to those fishermen who boast that they never pay for their fishing but get all they want through invitations. The elimination of these 'free loaders' was yet another benefit to the fishery. Likewise the rods felt the benefit, because they were not pestered by people who wanted to come as guests. The rods could explain that the new rules made guest tickets expensive and hard to obtain.

The final point in rule 10, concerning the exclusion of children, places the manager in yet another dilemma. To have the kids along or not to have them? And if you do, which ones? The rule must be applied fairly, and must be fully explained to the rods who are fathers of young children. The bulk of the members in every fishing club or private fishery are men and the human male, to a much greater degree than any other mammal, at times needs the companionship of other males, exclusive of women and children. I suppose this is because through hundreds of thousands of years, the human male spent most of his time off on hunting parties while the women and children stayed at home, in the cave, where they were safer and wouldn't hinder the hunting. There is still something of this in modern man's psyche. Civilized as he is, he still yearns for this all male group, especially when he is fishing and the hunting drive is strong.

Yes, I know you can point to the fact that many women fish these days and many children and so prove me wrong. But I would reply that the fisherwomen have themselves become hunters and so have the fisher children, and they are accepted in the hunting band.

When that argument has been either won or lost, we can raise a less controversial point. The bulk of the members in every fishing club or private fishery have demanding jobs. It does not matter if the work is in an office, a hospital, or beside a machine, it is all work after which relaxation is needed. The precious hours spent fishing should be a tranquil time, and one of the fishery manager's jobs, is to see that it is. The last thing a fisherman wants is a bunch of screaming children rushing about.

Outside our big cities on Sundays you can see whole families having an outing on the banks of rivers and canals. While the children romp and whoop about, mum sits and knits and dad dangles a bit of bread on a hook in the water. If he happens to catch a small fish every now and then, he is happy. When the family goes home in the evening, everybody has had a lovely time and dad is considered a great fisherman. There are families in all parts of the world who do just that and there is nothing wrong with it, but the fisherman who wants something more out of angling would not be satisfied, or even call it angling.

This type of fisherman generally enjoys meeting with others at lunch time to eat his sandwiches and discuss fishing conditions and the latest cricket results, but he likes plenty of elbow-room for his actual fishing. He cherishes solitude – he prefers that there should be nobody stamping along the banks, nobody coming every so often to ask how he is getting on, nobody to take his attention away from his fly or float. Unfortunately these are just the things that young children do. They cannot be expected to sit quietly for hours on end. They are bound to fidget and to start looking for some sort of activity. The father will reprimand them once or twice and make them sit down, but finally he finds that his own fishing is being spoilt, and he no longer bothers to watch his child. He doesn't think any real harm can come of letting the kid off the leash, and even if the kid does get into mischief, father doesn't think there is any *great* harm done. If the kid runs riot, which young children will if they think they can get away with it, the father is quite capable of telling the manager that it is *his* fault! I am not telling tall stories; I've seen it happen. I once had to haul a small child out of the lake because dad was busy fishing and mum was busy eating chocolates and reading a book in the family Rolls. Neither watched their child. I was very indignant, but they weren't bothered.

There are often children who long to learn to fish, and in the beginning at Two Lakes we allowed fathers to bring their young to teach them. It was not always very satisfactory. Because the father is a keen and skilful fisherman, it doesn't follow that he will be able to teach his child how to fish. He will probably begin enthusiastically enough, explaining how to go about things, but unless things go remarkably smoothly he is likely to get impatient with the child, lose his enthusiasm for teaching, and wander off to get on with his own fishing. The child will become discouraged and may develop an aversion to fishing. Many times I have come across children at Two Lakes, fishing listlessly on their own or, more often, climbing trees or throwing sticks and stones into the water and generally being a nuisance to other fishermen. When I have asked them why they had come if they were so little interested in fishing, they almost invariably replied that they had only come to please daddy.

When the father does take pains to teach his child how to fish, and the child becomes an ardent fisherman, it is inadvisable that the first lessons should take place on waters where there is a distinct possibility of large fish being caught. Fate is an inveterate practical joker, and if it should decree that the child's first fish be a monster, the child's angling pleasure will have been permanently corrupted. Subsequently, this child would sneer at the class of fishing to be found in a Scottish mountain loch, where the fish run to three to a pound. Youngsters should learn to fish their way up from small fish to bigger ones. They should be taught to cast properly, and to practice their casting until it is almost automatic.

Then there are those few boys and girls who are so keen to learn about angling that no difficulties whatsoever can keep them from the waterside. With great warmth we at Two Lakes think back to such children whom we have met through the years. I remember one boy aged nine years who came fishing with his father regularly. The boy was an excellent fisherman, with as much skill as many more experienced anglers. His manners were always impeccable and endeared him to everyone. He was treated as belonging to the hunting group, and everybody loved having him around.

Inexperienced anglers of all age-groups are obviously harmful to a fishery. They hook and lose so many fish, and even when they don't, they flog the water and cause panic amongst the fish. Often they won't admit that they are inexperienced. It is as well that the rods are informed that inexperienced anglers are unwelcome, then they won't be too casual about whom they ask to fish as guests.

11. Rods must inform their guests about these rules.

If a fisherman fishes a water for a number of years, he is inclined to forget the details of the rules. He simply remembers how many fish he may keep, what flies or bait are permitted, and if he is allowed to bring guests. So guests are let loose on the water with very vague instructions about what they can and cannot do. Often they are given no instructions at all. Countless times I have caught guests breaking the rules, and when their sins are pointed out to them, they blame their host for not having informed them. At Two Lakes we always ask the ticket holder if he has explained the rules when he arrives with a guest, and this saves a lot of embarrassment. A conscientious guest will enquire about the rules before he begins to fish. Some have a sense of responsibility, but most have not.

12. The use of boats, wading, and standing in the water is not permitted.

Boat fishing is mandatory in large, saucer-shaped lakes, but it is by no means so when the lakes are small and narrow. In fact, when they are fishing small lakes anglers often wistfully express a desire to fish from a boat so that they can get at all those fish, the biggest of course, which are in the middle of the lake. A manager would be ill-advised to fall in with such a request. If he did he would soon be gasping in disbelief at the sight of boats anchored in the middle of the lake with anglers casting towards the banks right in front of the bank fishermen.

For one season only, we allowed boat fishing at Two Lakes. The next season we returned promptly to fishing only from the banks. During the 'boating' year we had caught less fish than during the bank-fishing-only seasons. The reason must have been that the whole area of the lakes was being constantly disturbed, whereas when the anglers could fish only from the banks, they could never cover some stretches of water, even though the lakes are small. Out of casting range, the fish were not educated, and when the bank areas were fished out, the trout from the further reaches moved into the less populated bank areas. It must be so, because the fish had to come from somewhere.

On large lakes or reservoirs, boat fishing is necessary, and the expense of buying and maintaining boats is calculated into the price of a fishing ticket. On smaller lakes, the cost of boats and their maintenance cannot be justified. Granted, there should be opportunities for the fishermen to reach deeper water here and there, and to provide these opportunities, fishing piers can be built out from the banks. The piers can be of wood but they are quite costly even so and must have annual maintenance, in spite of which they don't last very long. On the other hand, with modern earth-moving machinery it is not too costly to have these piers made of banked soil. They are very solid, blend in with the surroundings and last indefinitely without any maintenance.

As to wading, in very large lakes and on some rivers, it is necessary if fish are to be caught. But in small lakes, particularly when they are long and narrow, it has to be considered carefully. Some fishermen say that a lot of tramping about in the water frightens the fish; they may be right, but we are more interested in other effects. In a well-run fishery, where care is taken to maintain a quantity of natural food for the fish, wading can do a lot of damage. After the introduction of the Jenkins Spire shell snails at Two Lakes (I will tell you all about that in a later chapter), the shallows became a black mass of countless snails. Trout, especially rainbow trout, are great snail eaters, and of the coarse fish, tench can specialize on snails. Therefore it is a pity when an angler, with his big feet, crushes to a pulp food which is provided to increase the size of the fish and keep them in good condition. Two Lakes has presented Jenkins Spire shell snails to other fisheries to help with increasing their natural food supply for the trout, and where the snail has approved of the new water, it has increased spectacularly. In these waters wading has also been stopped.

Wading can be dangerous as well. When the water is not very clear it is hard to estimate the depth and an angler who steps suddenly into deep water will find his boots waterlogged and if the ground is soft, as it often is, he can get into serious trouble, especially if he is elderly or not physically strong. After a few narrow escapes of this sort, by his anglers, a fishery manager will think twice about permitting wading.

13. No dogs are allowed.

In the first years of Two Lakes as a fishery, I never thought of objecting to anglers bringing their dogs. We are great dog-lovers, and we suspected other fishery managers who banned dogs from their water of being dog-haters.

As time went on, I learnt my lesson the hard way. An angler had a spaniel that loved water, and to the great pride of his master, the spaniel tried to retrieve trout when his master was playing them. In the commotion of fighting fish and swimming dog, the dog's master managed to lose a few of his hooked fish. I had to watch the circus, and felt none too happy about it. But then things got worse. The spaniel galloped over to the nearest fisherman and offered help in landing a hooked fish. The fisherman declined, first politely, then abusively, but the dog persisted, jumping into the water, and at this point my pot full of love and good will towards dogs boiled over spectacularly. Much as I dislike taking the blame for anything, I had to admit that initially it was my fault.

Then there are the little dachshunds. They are inclined to thieve. They sneak behind the angler, take a freshly caught trout, creep away again and have a good meal under some convenient bush. Does such a stolen fish, lost through no fault of the fisherman, count towards the total bag? I don't recall the ensuing arguments with much pleasure. Another dog carefully collected all the fish he could find and brought them to his master's car. When his master discovered the store, he had the embarrassing job of sorting out which fish belonged to whom. We once had a fisherman who brought his bitch when she was on heat, and his wife, who had presumably come to protect the bitch's honour, complained bitterly because our Butchy was persistently attentive. But this was an exception to the unwritten law, the rather incomprehensible law, that if a fisherman's dog annoys another fisherman, the manager is to blame; whereas if a fisherman's dog annoys the manager's dog, then it is the fisherman who is at fault.

And this brings us to the subject of the management's dogs. If angling dogs are required to behave with decorum (and we have quite a few angling dogs at Two Lakes in spite of the ban), then the resident dogs should also be made to behave. The resident dogs, of course, generally have a function to perform. In most places these days poaching is an ever present threat, and guard dogs are necessary. At Two Lakes we always have German Shepherd dogs (Alsatians). Many people are scared to death of the breed, particularly people who are up to no good, but these dogs are in fact intelligent, intensely loyal, incorruptible, and infinitely affectionate. We never consciously train our dogs, except for house training, because even as puppies they soon learn what we want, and to their way of thinking, what we want is the immutable law. They ignore the anglers' fish, their sandwiches, and the anglers themselves. They seem to know who has a right to fish, in other words who are the regular fishermen, and they recognize the cars. They don't start fights with angling dogs, so long as the angling dogs observe their territorial rights. The only time we have to remind them of their manners is when people try to come into the house uninvited. At night nobody is welcome at Two Lakes, and the dogs make this abundantly clear by their barking.

14. Day tickets, or any other short-term tickets are not issued.
Members of clubs or rods in private fisheries have a right to be informed if there are only season rods fishing, or if day-tickets or other short-term tickets are let as well. In the discussion of rule 5, the whole question of season-tickets and day-tickets has been explored.

15. Fishing time is from 9 a.m. to one hour after sunset.
Again, the policy of the management of large reservoir fisheries is often quite different from that of the smaller fisheries, in the matter of when a day's fishing can begin. It can be very exciting for the fishermen if they are permitted to arrive at the fishery in darkness and to start fishing when it is just getting light. By seven o'clock, before the staff arrives, some of the anglers have caught their limit and are on their way home. Have these fish been reported for the log-book? Have the staff seen the fish? What methods of angling did these early birds use? Every season the angling press is full of tales of the behaviour of fishermen who thought nobody had an eye on them. Keepers cannot be asked to work endless hours, and it is only when a fishery is large enough to employ several keepers that a shift system can be in operation. As it is, everybody knows the high jinks that the unobserved early-morning fisherman gets up to, and in the majority of trout fisheries fishing starts at eight or nine o'clock in the morning. What's more, just as many trout are caught as in fisheries which open at daybreak.

In coarse fisheries the situation is different. For several species of coarse fish, early morning fishing is the most rewarding, and it would be unfair of the management to deprive the angler of this pleasure. Moreover, in British coarse fish fisheries, supervision is not quite so necessary because no fish are taken away. In the fisheries of Continental Europe, where fish that are caught are taken away and eaten, supervision is necessary. The trend towards eating coarse fish may become common in Britain, as it once was, and then the management of these fisheries will be faced with a new set of problems.

Another important point is that in a well-managed fishery there must be some daylight hours when there are no anglers about. In heavily-fished trout waters there must be regular restocking during the fishing season, and the restocking should take place in the early morning. The fishermen are fully aware of this, and are in favour of the restocking taking place often and generously. But if they don't actually see it happening, they can, with glorious ambivalence, delude themselves into thinking that all the fish in their fishery are wild. Also, if they were to see the fish being put in, they would crowd around and flog that particular area mercilessly, in the hope of catching as many of the 'wild' trout as they can.

There are fisheries which deliberately advertise the fact that restocking will be carried out on such and such a day, and the exact time of the day is given. If the stocking is with small fish which must have time to grow on to catchable size, then such public stocking proves to the angler that the fish are there. Like justice, the stocking must be done and must be seen to be done.

It is during the early-morning hours, with no anglers about, that the keepers can go round collecting the empty bottles and beer cans, cigarette packets and polythene bags, to say nothing of chairs and fly boxes, priests, spectacles and, sometimes, rods and landing nets. Here at Two Lakes we are pestered by coots, and it is only in the early mornings, during the fishing season, that we can shoot the tiresome things, and shot they must be, otherwise they would overrun the lakes, and seriously disturb the fishing.

Season after season, week after week and day after day I have to remind the fishermen about the nine o'clock opening. No longer can we be tolerant of fishermen arriving early to be there when the hour strikes, for this became a sort of competition amongst some of the rods, who arrived earlier and earlier, and marched about with their rods and landing nets at the ready, prepared to rush down to the lakes on the dot of nine. Now they are not allowed through the gates a minute before nine and anybody who comes down the drive prematurely is sent back and has to go to the end of the queue of waiting cars. I think and hope that we have finally won on this matter but the going has been hard. I have been told that there is a similar competition amongst the regular commuters on the morning trains to London! At the end of the day there is a similar problem: the fishermen who won't go home. They are either unaware of or not interested in the fact that we have to shut the place up for the night and need some sleep. However, I think and hope, that we have finally won this one too by putting out the lights and saying 'Time, gentlemen, please!' at ten-thirty.

To repeat the little sermon printed at the end of our rules:

These regulations are resultant from the experience of the years in which the fishing has been in existence, and are set up as the best means of protecting the fishing. Protection of the fishing is a corollary of the protection of the rights of the fishermen. The primary aim of Two Lakes is to give the best it can in fishing, but to attain this object it needs the co-operation of the fishermen.

You will get co-operation, whole-hearted co-operation, if your fishing is really good because your rods don't want to lose out on it. In this chapter I have given many instances of the, shall we say, shortcomings of fishermen, and how to cope with them. I have said nothing about the virtues of anglers, because you will not have to protect your fishery against these. There are many who truly wish to play the game according to the rules and you will find that there are many who will appreciate your efforts at making their fishing enjoyable, who will grow to love your fishery and will be proud of it. They are the fishermen who make it all worth while, even when you are feeling particularly angry at some piece of outrageous behaviour.

5 River Management

In the past decade, interference in the management of angling waters has nowhere been so pronounced as on the rivers, interference caused by the increasing population and its effects; water abstraction, pollution, drainage, bank alterations, the lot. On a larger river, where boats and sometimes ships travel upstream and downstream continuously, a private owner or a club can do very little in management terms to affect angling. In this case the Water Authority is the only body capable of making any significant impression. In waters where so many interests have a right of use, angling will always be a poor relation. Some of these rivers still provide reasonable coarse fishing, often for the match fishermen, but that is about as far as the angling possibilities can be stretched.

Financial Matters

We turn to the smaller rivers, fifteen, twenty and even fifty metres wide. The odd canoe paddling down the river will not upset the fishing critically but most problems of interference will be very much to the fore. In discussing how a small river can be managed for fishing, it is important first to understand the financial possibilities of a river that can provide good sport. Start, therefore, by finding out what you can take in subscriptions on a given stretch of river. When this has been determined, and if you decide to go ahead, you must see that the river is managed (with regard to weed, food creature and amenities), in such a way that it reaches its fullest potential in attracting anglers.

So many people or clubs dream of owning a stretch of river. The scarcer good river fishing becomes, the more it will be sought after. If a stretch of river comes on to the market for purchase, or on a long lease, the temptation is great and there are too many who plunge headlong into the untried angling venture. Even if a river is healthy and has a good reputation in the angling world, the length of the stretch is of paramount importance. Acquiring a few hundred yards may realize somebody's dream of glory and satisfy the ego, and also provide a trout now and then, but the few hundred yards could never provide good sport for a group of fishermen. Another great mistake is the buying or leasing of one bank only. Even if the river is very wide, there are still too many management problems of which one is stocking, and most rivers these days are stocked. I know of a fishery which was launched with the highest hopes on two miles of single bank on a river averaging fifteen metres in width. An agreement was made with the owners of the opposite bank for co-operative management. But it didn't work out, and the endless bickering spoilt the fishing for everybody. Now both parties are trying to buy each other out.

Nothing less than a mile (1609 metres) should be considered a manageable stretch for a fishery that is to provide good sport. A mile can give reasonable fishing for twenty-one rods, each coming one day a week. The price would be rather high, and here let me say that the figures I quote were obtained at the time of writing this book and would be proportionately greater today. This fact must be allowed for in any calculations. The river must be divided into beats, and the manager will have to work out a rotation system to give every fisherman an equal chance as the beats will vary in their fish holding capacity. On a river that has a good reputation – if it is a chalk stream so much the better – the price would be £300 for each rod. Assuming that all twenty-one rods are let, the income would be £6300. If the manager's objective is an average weight of 1½ lbs for the total bag in the coming season, the average season total of fish for each member should be nearly one hundred trout. If half the stock trout are bought in from trout farms and the other half is grown on from yearlings in the fishery's own stewponds, the cost of the stocking would be about £2000. This estimate is on the high side, but may serve to dampen undue optimism.

The second largest expenditure would be the wages for a full-time keeper, which, at the time of writing, would be £2000. This would include the price of renting accommodation for him in the *top* Rain shelter on the right is simply four posts with a corrugated iron roof, and with a seat inside. Whenever possible their unsightliness should be hidden by placing them amongst bushes beside a path.

centre All dams must be wide enough to carry a road. Vehicles should be able to reach most parts of the fishery to facilitate stocking and other activities.

below Reinforced concrete lintels (as used over wide factory doors) make excellent and permanent bridges requiring no upkeep.

above Alsatians are a must for all well-keepered angling waters. Poachers and vandals have a healthy respect for this breed.

below This rather ancient looking wheelbarrow has proved through the years to be most suitable for work along a river. One-board-wide plank bridges and narrow paths are easy to negotiate. The construction of the barrow permits a bath full of water and fish, or any other heavy load, to be pushed with a minimum of effort.

nearest village. Should the fishery be lucky enough to own a keeper's cottage, it has a great advantage. But the upkeep of the cottage must be included in the calculations. The rates will vary considerably from area to area, and a realistic estimate would be in the region of £400. This sum is the rate for the whole fishery.

Then, in every fishery, there are a hundred and one other expenditures. These OTHERS include occasional labour, printing, advertising and tools and can be expected to reach about £800. Now the total expenditure runs to £5200, and when this sum is deducted from the income of £6300, the fishery is left with a profit of £1100.

If a private owner runs such a fishery for a profit and hopes to make a living, he is worse off than is his keeper. Of course, if he is keen and capable, he could run the fishery himself, and so save the keeper's wages, which would raise the profit to £3100. There are such fisheries, but they are run by unusually dedicated people.

Even a club with no profit motive can be pleased if there is a surplus, as this can always be used for improving the fishery. To use the surplus money for reducing the price of the rods, however, would be foolish in the extreme. Fishing club members are very quick to suggest this measure. The committee responsible for the management of the club should be adamant in refusing even to consider it. Originally, anglers were attracted to this particular club because it had a reputation for having a high annual bag, with a reasonable average weight, and the possibility of catching some very big fish. It takes years to build up such a reputation, and everything could be jeopardized through such short-sighted measures. Members must be continually reminded that they can only expect to get what they pay for.

If one mile of river is stocked with trout and has good holding potential most trout will remain. But should this stretch of river not be especially attractive to trout, most of them will vanish upstream and downstream, to the delight of the neighbours who have more suitable stretches of river.

A fishery owning two miles, both banks included, is in a much better position. There will be more variation in the shape of the river, with the result that the beats can be longer, and more interesting, and thirty-five rods can be accommodated comfortably, each paying £400. Anglers paying this amount of money are justified in expecting more for their subscription than are fishermen on a one mile long fishery. As they will be fishing on a one day a week basis, in all fairness they must be allowed to send someone in their place if they cannot fish on their allotted day, and they must be granted more guests. This is quite the opposite of what I had to say on the subject when we were discussing the rules in the previous chapter, but £400 for a rod entitles the fisherman to some privileges!

Thirty-five season rods paying £400 each provide the fishery with an income of £14,000. More trout for the fishermen means more spent on stocking. As there will be a second keeper, the extra help will mean that more small trout can be brought on in the stew ponds. Nonetheless, stocking will still cost around £4500. This second keeper will be paid £1500, so with the head keeper's £2000, the fishery will be spending £3500 on wages. The rates may come to £800, and all the other odd items of expenditure must be kept to £900, which will be possible because the second keeper will, to a great extent, take the place of occasional labour. The total expenditure comes to £9700, which, subtracted from the income of £14,000, leaves the fishery with a profit of £4300.

Should the fishery be longer, say three miles, the profitability increases, but, more important, so does the sport for the angler. Taking the figure of twenty-one fishermen on the one mile long fishery, three miles could accommodate sixty-three anglers. But, as the price for a season ticket will be £500, the rods must be given more value for money than they would have on the two mile fishery. Therefore, not sixty-three anglers, but only forty-nine anglers will be fishing on the three mile fishery and will bring in £24,500. They will have more space, and the opportunity to catch more trout than will the fishermen on the first two fisheries we have given as examples, and the average weight of the trout must be heavier. The total cost of stocking will be about £8000; the head keeper needs another helper who will cost another £1500, and this brings the cost of the three keepers to £5000. The third man is necessary not only to help in keepering the river, but also to attend to the extra trout in the stewponds. Rates will have gone up to £1200, and other expenses should not be more than £1000. With yet another keeper working, many jobs previously given to outside contractors or occasional labour can now be done entirely by the staff. Total expenditure will be £15,200, which deducted from the £24,500 taken in from the rods leaves £9300 for the owner, if it is a private fishery, or for the club's piggy bank. The figures demonstrate again that the larger the fishery, the sounder the finances, and this applies to lake fisheries as well. As an aside, just as these lines were being written, it was announced in a news bulletin on the radio that the official figures for the average wage in Britain is £2500 per year. This is of interest in relation to the above. It would be of interest, as well, to know when the law of diminishing returns would come into play in a large fishery. There is no information about this, presumably because nobody has ever had the opportunity of gaining control of a fishing area which is large enough. It must be remembered that all the figures which have been given can be thrown into disarray if the fishery is not fully booked.

Fortunately, there are many private fisheries and clubs which have been in existence for fifty years, and in some cases much longer, and they are always fully booked. It is the expertise of the people in charge which spells success. Give members the best that you possibly can in fishing. Never save on the wrong items of expenditure. Correct stocking is of utmost importance, and a knowledgeable and friendly staff. For a time, fishermen may forgive the management for a miserable fishing hut, 'lame' seats, muddy and overgrown paths, but for fishless water and a sullen unhelpful staff, never.

A club with the principle of not making any profit whatsoever and, instead, keeping the members' subscriptions to the lowest possible figure, will find sooner rather than later that they will land in trouble, as I have already pointed out. If there is never any surplus income, then there are no resources for dealing with emergencies. The members will be the first to blame the management for not having made allowances for unexpected happenings. If for some reason it proves impossible to keep to the level of the subscriptions as suggested in the three examples, there must be reorganization of the rod arrangements. Full rods can be halved, or even become quarter rods. The bag limit can be reduced, or if the nature of the river permits, the length of the beats can be reduced. If the stocking costs remain the same with regard to numbers of fish and average weights, and more anglers want to share, they will all have less. If the same standard of sport is demanded by more anglers paying less money, it cannot be provided. Standards are inevitably lowered. This is precisely what happened on some fisheries on the east coast of the United States of America. As the angling pressure near great centres of population became overwhelming, the fisheries with limited membership were constrained to take on more and more anglers. Sport dwindled down to trout weighing even less than half a pound each. Subscriptions are now low, and everybody can afford the price. Most anglers know nothing better, so they enjoy it.

A skilled fishery manager, given a reasonable stretch of water, can provide the type of sport for which anglers are prepared to to pay. There is the very expensive fishing and that which is very cheap, and somewhere between the two lies the answer to what many anglers consider good trout fishing.

If the price of a rod on a fishery is as low as £50, and even if the fishing is good value for money, there will still be some who cry, 'I can't afford it.' That depends. What about anglers who visit their pub and without the slightest hesitation buy a round of expensive drinks for their companions? These same anglers object strenuously when the subscription of their fishing club must be raised a few pounds annually. The price of drinks in the pub on a very few evenings will cover the increased club subscriptions handsomely. The reason for this disinclination to pay a fair price for fishing may be that there still lingers in all of us the idea that fishing should be free as it used to be in the distant past. Anybody should be able to understand that fishing cannot be free in this overcrowded world of ours. Whether fishing is cheap or expensive, is a matter of how you look at it. Once again, I have a little story from Two Lakes to illustrate this point.

A young man in his late twenties, with a not very highly paid job and a wife and family, took a season ticket at Two Lakes. He was a first-class fisherman and always caught fish. On one of his visits, he brought his wife with him. While her husband was fishing, the young woman sat rather forlornly on a bench watching him from afar. Because she looked so lonely, and because she was pretty, I went over to her for a chat. During the conversation, she told me that they were people who really could not afford to fish at Two Lakes: they had a mortgage to pay off, there were many things they needed for their home, and their children grew out of clothes very quickly. But her husband loved fishing so much that she had not the heart to suggest that he should give it up. As I have said, she was pretty, but she was also intelligent, so I thought it worth while to give her a lesson in fishery economics.

I pointed out that as her husband was a good fisherman and a successful one, he always brought home a good number of trout. This weight of fish, if bought in a fish shop, would amount to nearly three-quarters of the price of the fishing ticket. Each time her husband came home with trout she would not need to buy either fish or meat, and those fish which could not be eaten at once went into her deep freeze to obviate some future visits to the fishmonger or butcher. Moreover, as her husband was a heavy smoker, I suggested that she should try to wean him from his fags a little, and aside from safeguarding his health, the cash saved would make up for the remaining quarter of the price of his fishing ticket. All without him becoming a pot hunter. She perked up immediately.

At the beginning of this chapter, I said that the first point for discussion would be the financial rewards that we can expect from a fishery on a river. This we have done for the average river not, of course, a river such as the Mississippi nor, at the opposite extreme, a stream of the size that a fisherman could jump over. Such tiny streams are interesting to fish, but only by the odd person. Rods cannot be let, and only a miniature fishing club would rent a stream so small. Notwithstanding, there are many such streams, a few steps in width, where enterprising fishermen have made little wire netting dams, waterfalls made from old paving slabs, deep holes here, gravel runs there. They provide amusement and, now and then, a rather small trout but it is not fishing in the accepted sense of the word. I have met people who fish such small streamlets who tell everybody what marvellous sport they had on *their* little *river*, but given half a chance they soon vanish to a water which holds more and larger trout, and where they have the space to cast.

Altering a Stream and Making it Fishable

When a stream is sufficiently wide so that even a record holder in long jump cannot hop over it, then this water, with intelligent management, can provide sport for quite a number of members. Should the stream be rather straight, as quite often happens in low land without much tree cover, then the first job is to alter the run of it. If you leave it straight, an angler approaching the water is able to see another angler fishing there already, even if he is quite far distant, and will say, 'Oh no, there is somebody fishing there already.' Figure 25 shows this scene, while Figure 26 illustrates the same stream after there have been some alterations and some trees have been planted. The anglers are fishing much closer together, but they cannot see one another. A machine can alter the flow of the stream into bends, pools, and straight runs. Fast-growing trees have been planted on the bends in order to obstruct the view yet to leave sufficient room for fly fishing, though on a coarse fishing river, less room would be needed.

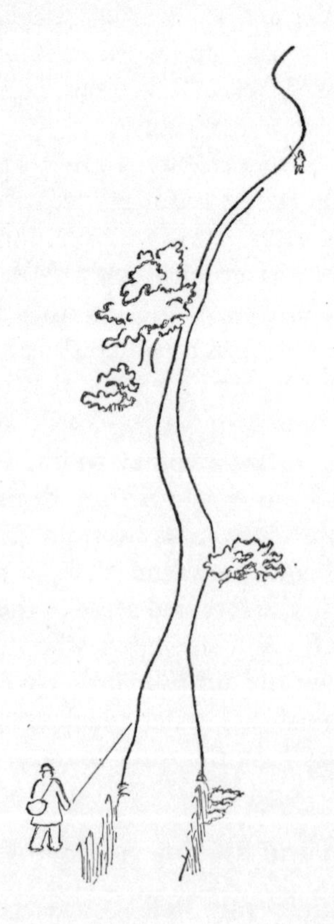

FIGURE 25

Don't forget that before altering the stream in this manner, two things must be settled. Whoever owns the land must give permission, and the Water Authority must give permission. Often there must also be permission from the planning authorities. Much preparatory work is required, including meetings with all the parties concerned and the drawing up of plans. It is as well not to have a committee making the plans because there will be too many ideas bandied about and too many squabbles over which ideas are best. Similarly, it is not a good thing to have only one man making the plans. It is best that two or three men should be left to produce sketches, having first gone over the stream, up and down its entire length. As I have said, bends in the stream must be made with fast gravelly runs and wide deep pools. If the fall of the land permits, waterfalls can be created.

The best machine for such work would be a dragline. Some

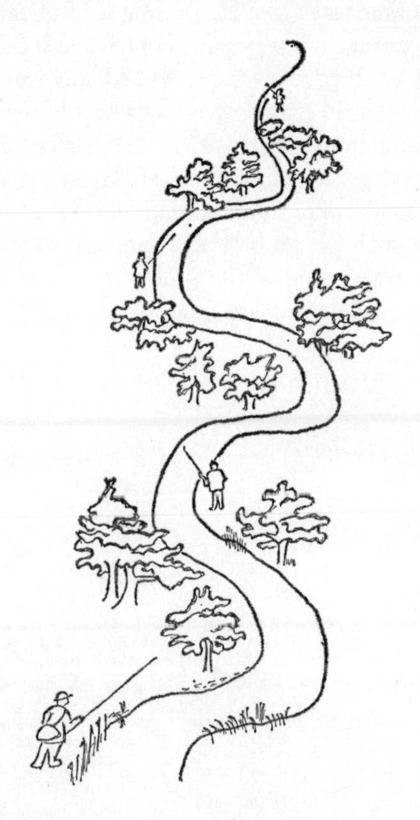

FIGURE 26

stretches of the bank may be waterlogged, in which case the machine can work on mats. These are generally several old railway-sleepers bolted together, and they are placed step by step in front of the machine as they are needed. The mats provide a surface for the distribution of the weight of the machine and prevent it from sinking into the swampy ground. The operator may be an expert at handling his dragline, but most likely he will never have done a similar job and will need someone constantly in attendance to tell him how the stream bed is to be shaped.

Railway sleepers or concrete blocks placed across the stream can create waterfalls, and at the same time increase the depth of water behind them. You must get permission from the Water Authorities for these obstructions and because they are not at all easy to remove, the Water Authorities are sometimes reluctant to give it.

There are other ways to raise the water level and at the same time to make a waterfall and these contrivances can be removed easily if need be. Figure 27 shows forked sticks pushed into the bank, with the forked part protruding towards the centre of the stream and held in position with a post driven into the river bed. Brushwood piled against these sticks on the upstream side will quickly collect more debris, and the water level will rise. Shrimps love such places and will increase in great numbers. On the downstream side of the sticks, trout and other fish will find good cover and plenty of food. The stream is pressed into

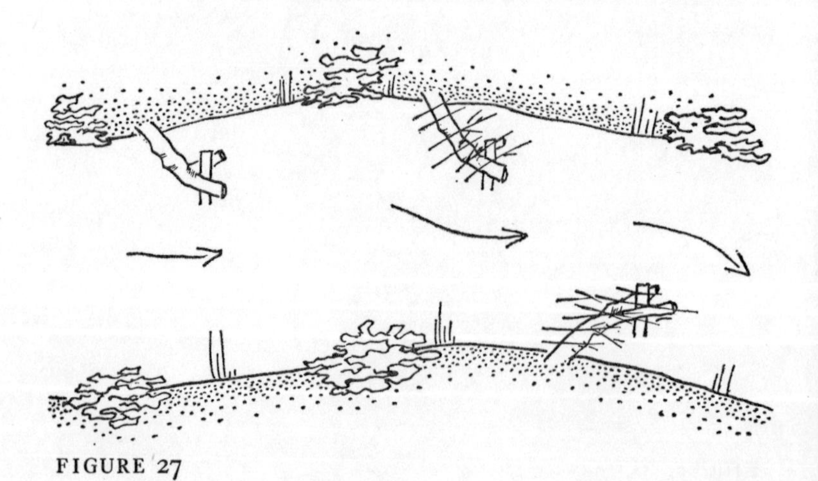

FIGURE 27

a narrow channel between the sticks which gives it a lively appearance. But you should not overdo the trick of altering the flow. In a stretch of several hundred metres it is sufficient to have two such combinations of sticks every ten metres.

Where a waterfall is required over the whole width of the stream, wire netting nailed to posts which are driven into the stream bed is cheap and effective. Again, the wire netting stops all the debris and raises the water level and you must be careful that the wire is laid down on the upstream side of the bed of the stream for a metre or more, otherwise the water will find its way underneath. Furthermore, the wire must continue on the upstream side of both banks or the water will find a way around it. Such wire netting dams are not too easily removed, but they do not last more than two or three seasons. Another, very simple dam across the whole stream can be made of single strands of barbed wire. On both sides of the stream a post is driven into the bank, and the barbed wire is fastened between them, or between two trees if they are correctly placed. There must be sufficient tension so that the wire is about 30 cm above the water. On the upstream side, at an obtuse angle, sticks are laid against the wire. Any brushwood or brambles gathered from clearing a path along the stream are laid across the sticks and soon our old friend the floating debris will do the rest, creating a rather flimsy-looking dam. The water will rise quickly and fall over the dam in a waterfall. Again, several things have been achieved by this contraption. Above it, the shallow, fishless part of the stream becomes deeper and can hold fish. Beneath the new waterfall there will be well-aerated water, and the water will have dug a deep hole right across the stream, providing another good place for fish to lie. Moreover, the brushwood is a haven for snails and shrimps (see Figure 28).

Because this single strand of barbed wire is so flimsy, the dam can be removed very quickly. This, in conjunction with the fact that initially it cost practically nothing in materials and only a few hours of the keeper's time, is consistent with the necessity of keeping down running expenses, which is always of concern in a fishery. That these dams are effective has been proved in many fisheries. Since maintenance in a fishery is such a big item on the expenses sheet, some of the dams described in textbooks are uneconomic. The expenditure cannot be justified

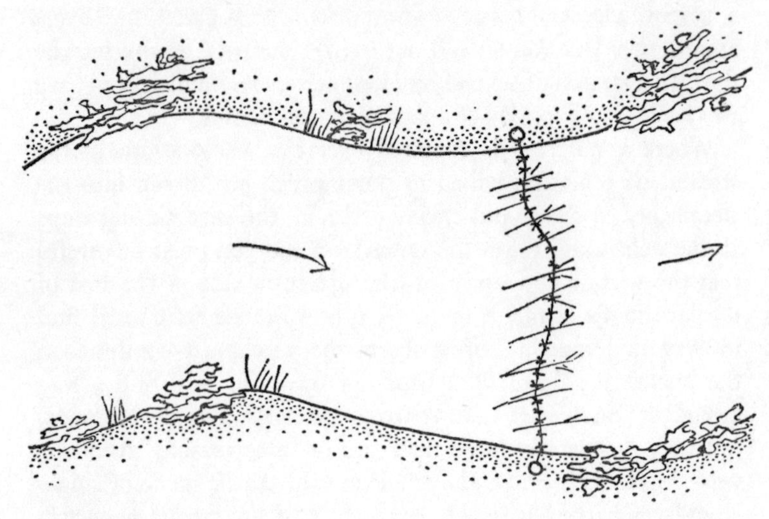

FIGURE 28

when there are contrivances which are cheaper and do the job just as well. But do not forget, that all the improvements which have been described are suitable only on small streams.

In hilly or mountainous areas there are usually large stones and boulders in the stream, and these can be shuffled around to create small dams. The first floods in the autumn will push these away, but at least they will have served their purpose during the summer fishing season.

Weed

The next item in the welfare of the stream or river is to look to the management of the underwater weed. This must be carefully balanced between the extremes of no weed at all, in which case the fishery would be in a sorry state, and of so much weed the water is clogged and there can be no fishing. Plenty of weed keeps the water level high, brings oxygen into the water and provides cover for the fish and a habitat for the endless small creatures which the fish feed upon. Sometimes weed also prevents bank erosion. Where the strong current flows around a bend in the river and hits the opposite bank the bank gradually erodes and then collapses. Here is the place for a permanent weed bed.

But the flow of the water must not be obstructed. Enough

channels must be cut through the weed beds to allow a free flow. Then there is also the fisherman to be considered. Farming and other interests must always come first but, granted this, there is no reason why an attempt to cut the weed should not be made so as to give the angler a chance as well. The compromise of conflicting interests in weed management has been effected admirably in the chalk streams, where fishing interests carry considerable weight. Other rivers can only emulate as closely as possible this example.

Figure 29 illustrates the different patterns. In practice such

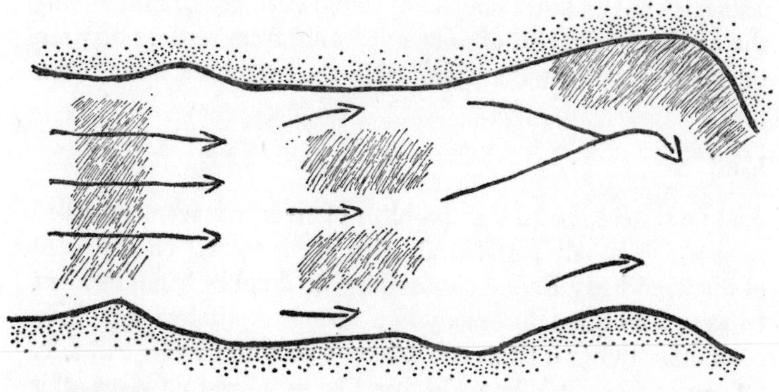

FIGURE 29

elegantly shaped patterns can be cut only in the weed beds of rivers where wading is possible. Where the water is too deep for wading, and the cutting of the weed is done from a boat, the weed-beds tend to be of a rather less distinctive shape. A scythe and a hoe are first-class tools in shallow water, and if a scythe is used from a boat, the handle must be very long, depending on the depth of the river. A much better tool for very deep stretches is a chain scythe, despised by many people as destructive. It is not the chain scythe that does the damage, it is the men handling it. If the chain scythe is worked upstream it will cut the weed right down to the river bed. When it is worked downstream it will not cut so deep and will leave cover for underwater life, cover which also prevents the fish from deserting that particular stretch. Moreover, the working party with the chain scythe must cut a certain length in the described manner, and then leave a band of weed across the river untouched.

Should the water level still be too high, then these bands must be topped off to permit the water to flow more freely.

Weed cutting in rivers must be carried out in co-operation with other fisheries. On some rivers there are fishery associations which agree on the times for weed cutting. Fresh cut weed floating downstream from other fisheries can ruin a day's fishing for many anglers.

Between twenty-five per cent and forty per cent of the surface area of a river should hold weed. If it is cut as shown in the last sketch, it will serve its purpose of holding fish and aquatic creatures, of helping to regulate the flow of the stream, of giving a sluggish river a faster flow between the weed beds, of improving the hatches of fly, and of preventing mud from settling between the beds where the water, confined by the weed beds, flows faster.

Mud

And now we come to that problem of river management called mud which is only partly dealt with in the correct management of the weed beds. Before condemning mud out of hand, it might be as well to question exactly how serious a problem it is. Like most other things it turns out to have a good side and a bad side. Of course when it is knee-deep and being stirred up gives off a nasty smell – poisonous gases which are harmful to aquatic life – it seems wholly bad. But even then we should not scorn our original cradle, the primeval slime of ancient days: and a little mud, a few centimetres thick, is beneficial amongst the weeds as it gives them nourishment and provides the right conditions for some forms of aquatic life.

In the enormous carp farms, with pond areas of hundreds of hectares, ponds with a clean clay or sandy bottom are considered to be sterile. A thin layer of mud is essential to provide suitable living conditions for many of the creatures that make carp farming possible. Of course, a fast trout stream cannot be compared with a sheet of still water holding carp; in fish farming they are at the opposite ends of the scale. However, the fanatical hatred of mud harboured by many managers of trout streams is a little overdone.

If the checker-board patterns of weed cutting give us plenty of fast runs over clean gravel, mud will most likely collect in the weed. So, the following year, the weed beds are encouraged in other places in order to give the stream a chance to wash the mud away.

Very deep and sluggish stretches with no weed must be dealt with by other methods. Sheep hurdles, or sheets of corrugated iron, are set against posts driven into the river bed. If these obstacles are sited so that the current is thrown from one side of the river to the other, great quantities of mud can be moved very easily, and when the desired effect has been achieved, the obstacles can be set up in a new pattern to shift the remaining mud. This is practicable only when the river has a strong flow, and is best done in the early spring.

An old-fashioned method, which under some conditions still has its uses, is the mud pan. If the mud is on the solid side, well and good. But these days it is very expensive to remove it with mud pans if it is of a porridge-like consistency. Instead there are pumps designed to suck mud from the river bed, and these can be hired at reasonable rates from plant hire firms. In a short time long stretches of river can be cleared with these pumps, and the mud can be deposited on adjoining farmland. Most farmers will agree to take it as it enriches the soil.

When discussing weed control, I said that when a strong current flows around a bend in the river, the outer side, taking the force of the current, should be protected by a permanent weed bed to help check erosion. The opposite side of the bend – the inside, so to speak – is a place where mud often collects. If the mud is dragged out it will help only for a short time because fresh mud will accumulate. It would be better to drive strong posts into the river bed in front of the mud bed and then to fill in behind the posts with rubble or chalk. As the bend has been made narrower, the current will flow faster and will not allow the mud to settle.

Another notorious place for mud to build up is on wide sections of smallish rivers. The width of the river is too great relative to the flow of water, and these parts act as settling beds. Here the best remedy is to make the river narrower, but remember that this counts as a major alteration and the Water Authorities will have to approve it. The cost of such an undertaking will be considerable and you have to weigh it carefully against the possible advantages to be gained from the improvement.

If you do decide to go ahead, one way to make the river narrower would be to drive piles into the river bed at the line of the proposed new bank and then between the piles and the old bank, fill in with anything handy in the way of material. The mud can then be dredged with mud pans on to the new bank and left to drain and consolidate. Again, it would be cheaper and quicker to pump the mud from the river. Sometimes a dragline is used for such operations but this machine is not very efficient for dealing with soupy mud which seeps out of the bucket and gaily splashes back into the river. A serious drawback to using a dragline is that the nice solid river bed underneath the mud can be loosened by the bucket, and in the future the mud will settle more readily.

A final word of warning about the combined problem of weeds and mud: if permanent weed beds are established there is the danger of more and more mud collecting there, and in time rushes take root, and an area of half-bog and half-water is created. You must watch for this development in permanent weed beds, especially in river bends.

Stocking

Here we come to an area in management which is fraught with contradictions, prejudices, folklore and downright lies. It should be very simple: as ye stock so shall ye reap. It should be simple, but it isn't. Before we enter this jungle of controversy, I should first remind you that the river must be prepared in order to be habitable for the fish. When we are discussing the management of weed I mentioned the problem of giving the fish natural living conditions.

If, say, a dragline has removed every hiding place in a river, be it weed, tree stumps, boulders, underwater banks, or even a discarded bath tub, the river has become a watery desert, from the fish's point of view. The drainage problem has perhaps been solved and the water gallops without hindrance in its obstacle free bed down towards the sea but there is nowhere for the fish to spawn, nowhere for them to feed and nowhere for them to find shelter from the strong current. If, by chance or design, the entire length of the river has not been reduced to a drainage channel, and there are still some unspoilt or well-keepered stretches remaining, the fish will promptly migrate to these happier parts. So, beware of stocking a stretch of river which the fish have abandoned; be it with ova, fry, fingerlings, takable fish, or outsize fish, you could have saved yourself the bother. 'As ye stock so shall ye reap' is as inappropriate here as in the case of the dwindling number of rivers where modern machinery has not yet carried out 'improvements', and which still provide a natural habitat for fish. Being healthy and unaffected by human activity, they need no stocking. They have plenty of food and natural spawning facilities. If the number of fishermen, and their bag limit, is restricted, there need be no restocking at all. Such rivers are the exception, and most fishermen only encounter them in their dreams.

This book is concerned with fisheries close to large centres of population, and we must be realistic. We cannot afford the wild fish dream. Some people deceive themselves into believing implicitly in the pseudo-wild. The cry goes up: 'Stock with ova or fry and you have wild fishing as near as damnit.' This is nonsense. As a matter of fact, stocking with eggs *was* the means of introducing European brown trout into Asia, Australia and the United States. Likewise, the American rainbow trout was introduced into other countries, and all this was quite some time ago. The waters stocked suffered no angling pressure and the species became naturalized subjects of the existing fish stock. As angling pressure increased, fisheries had no time to wait for the fish to grow to catchable size. But after about 1960, stocking with ova or fry was carried out only in out of the way streams, mostly in mountainous areas where not too many anglers ventured to fish, or on waters so vast that they cannot be fished intensively.

Somebody will ask, 'What has the introduction, years ago, of brown trout into Asia or of rainbow trout into Britain, to do with wild fishing?' The answer is that there is no longer time to wait for fry to grow to catchable size. Besides, what exactly is a wild fish? You need only read the angling press to see that this burning question has not yet been answered to everybody's satisfaction.

It comes down to the fact that stocking with fry is not, in most cases, the answer. This means that stocking must be done with sizeable fish and what is sizeable will depend on local expectations.

Some clubs are satisfied with half-pounders, while others want pounders, two-pounders or much larger fish. As I have said before, the fishery manager can, within reason, provide the type of fishing members are prepared to pay for.

For actual stocking, the entire consignment of fish should not be dumped in at one place, just because there is easy access from the road. Rather, as many places as are practicable should be selected beforehand and the number of fish for each spot should be correctly estimated. And it is not a bad idea for the manager to go along the river a few days later and see how the fish have settled down. If they haven't and most of them have vanished, it means that the preparation of the river was not satisfactory from the fish's point of view.

As I have already pointed out in the chapter on fishing rules, it is sometimes found to be worth while to stock fry in fisheries where only catchable size fish are stocked. When these fry are growing up in the river (not in stewponds) they feed on tiny creatures; they seldom take an artificial fly. When they have grown larger and take bigger food, then they will also take an artificial fly. By this time, most of these little trout will be of eatable size and should not be returned to the water, but should be killed and taken home for breakfast. A few, a very few, will manage against all odds to survive from season to season, and if there is sufficient natural food in the water, to grow big. There are instances of brown trout having survived to grow into big fish, but a scattering of survivors does not prove that fry stocking is a roaring success, and the answer to all future stocking problems.

But if, in spite of the discouraging things I have had to say, a fishery is determined to stock with small fish, here are a few suggestions. Much depends on local conditions. I have gone through reports from angling clubs both British and overseas, and the stocking figures that are quoted differ widely. So I have taken the average as a rough guide. A stream with plenty of food can be stocked in April and May with four three to four month old fry per square metre, or yearlings can be stocked at the rate of six to eight per hundred square metres. These stockings should be on an annual basis. Furthermore, you must remember that on average, smaller streams carry a greater head of trout than do rivers.

Most of the other contradictions, prejudices, etc. on the subject of stocking have been dealt with in the chapter on the fishing rules, so entangled are the two subjects.

Hatcheries and Stewponds in a Fishery

When the subject of stocking comes under discussion at a committee meeting of a fishing club, there is invariably somebody who suggests that the club should build its own hatchery and stewponds. What fun it would be to strip one's own trout, to lay down the eggs, and to see the alevins hatch; then to raise from fry the big trout for stocking the club's waters. Indeed, it would be the greatest fun, but for how long? If all the work is done by eager amateurs, there will be no wage bills, but generally speaking there will be no trout either. Amateurism, as I have said before, is seldom consistently successful.

The efficient and therefore successful running of a hatchery is a full-time job for a professional. There are few instances of success where the work was left to the enthusiasm of the members. Thinking back over the years I can recall only one club where this was so. This club had a member who was physically handicapped and was employed in a nearby factory as a night watchman. He took on the hatchery. With great keenness he spent all his free time looking after it, and later on looking after the young fish. Eventually, for one reason or another, he had to give up. The club struggled on for a few seasons, and then closed the hatchery down. Small trout were bought in from a trout farm and fed on in the stewponds until they were the required size.

Only in special circumstances is the setting-up of a hatchery justified. The first consideration must be: Is it worth the expense and the trouble? If there is no spring which will supply suitable water, a borehole must be sunk. A vermin-proof building must be put up for the hatchery and egg trays and long rearing troughs must be installed. And what about the work involved in a hatchery? It must be visited several times a day for checking the water supply, for removing dead ova and, later, for keeping a sharp eye on the fry. The committee members who are most persistent about setting up a hatchery are generally the last people who are prepared to give any time to help with the work.

It is only clubs with a large membership that can afford a keeper with relevant experience, and I would stress that the keeper *must* be experienced, otherwise there is a strong possibility that part, if not all of the ova or fry will be lost through ignorance.

Two Lakes has no hatchery, but we have a number of stewponds which we use for growing yearlings to larger fish, the yearlings having been bought from trout farms which have the facilities and labour to support a hatchery. The advantage of the stewponds is that there are always some trout in the fishery as an insurance against the trout farms not being able to deliver trout for stocking on the dates agreed. Many small clubs and private fisheries have stewponds, and grow on yearlings; but this can be expensive. Mind you, if the expenses of labour, pond space, etc., are not included in the reckoning, then the growing on of yearlings can be cheaper than buying the same size in fish from a trout farm. Those who have no expenses of labour, pond space, etc., are indeed blessed. But on the whole, if careful records of expenses are kept, it will generally be found that growing on yearlings is not significantly cheaper than buying fish for stocking from a trout farm.

If a fishery has no stewponds it is not too difficult to have these built. If they are along a river or on very low-lying land, they can be dug out by machine It is not wise to site the ponds too far away from the keeper's cottage or from other habitation as they need regular attention and also protection against pilfering and vandalism. Poachers not only net isolated ponds, but lower the water, and even drain them completely, through the hatch system. It is always possible to instal an alarm system, but this is not effective if the stews are too isolated. So if you are venturing into building stews, it is best to site them sensibly from the beginning. We are very cautious at Two Lakes: our stewponds are right in front of the house.

The ponds can be earthen, having simply been dug out by machine. The usual bowl shape is best as the water flow runs over the whole pond; but longish rectangles have the advantage of being easier to net. At Two Lakes we could not have earthen ponds, because although many parts of the property have solid clay soil, there are areas of sand and gravel. Around the house it is pure sand which would not hold the water, so the stewponds had to be constructed entirely of concrete. This was much more expensive than simply digging out a longish pond in the ground, but there are advantages: concrete ponds are easier to clean, easier to net, and should disease strike, they can be emptied one hundred per cent and dried out completely. Their fish carrying capacity is also higher than that of an equivalent sized earthen pond; for they can be cleaned at regular intervals by a suction pump (similar to those pumps used to clean swimming pools), and as this removes any mud or rotting matter which would use up oxygen, the ponds can hold more trout. They are not too difficult to build and need not be deeper than one metre. From the inlet of the water to the outlet there should be a slight fall in the floor which will permit complete draining and make cleaning easier. The outlet can be a small monk. Because the monk need be only just over one metre high, it can be made of wood in an earthen pond. In our concrete stews we have outflows basically similar to the monk, but modified to our special purposes.

The feeding of the trout in stewponds these days is mostly with pellets. When pellets were first introduced I was very doubtful that they would be as satisfactory as meat, white fish, or liver. (We are inclined to take an anthropomorphic view of the likes and dislikes of animals, and this includes appreciation of good food.) However, after many years of experience with pellets, I can affirm that the fish thrive on them, through all stages of their development. If the pellets are of first-class quality, the results are highly satisfactory.

There are a few suggestions I can make in the interests of economy. If you buy an amount of pellets which is sufficient for your needs, and certainly it is cheaper to buy larger quantities than a bag at a time, find out from the manufacturer how long you can store them. Some of the vitamins deteriorate when they are kept too long. An amateur is tempted to be rather lavish with the food, and it is better to remember that a little and often produces a better conversion rate than does one huge meal. Remember, too, to stop feeding when you see spare pellets floating about in the stewpond. You don't want to feed the rats, who soon learn that the pellets fetch upon the sides of the pools, and are very clever at thinking up ways to get them out of the water. Because there is so much waste through hand-feeding, some fishery managers insist on a large spoon being used. Feeding pellets by hand means that every time a handful of them is taken out of the bucket, some fall to the ground, a man I know who runs his rod fishery to earn a living, was feeding by hand as I was standing beside him, and I remarked on all the pellets falling on to the ground. He said he kept a few chickens to pick up the waste pellets. But this is rather an expensive way of producing eggs when, at the time of writing, a ton of trout pellets costs £250 and a ton of chicken food costs £80!

A labour-saving (and pellet-saving) way of feeding, is to use automatic feeders though it wouldn't really be economic to instal these where there are only a small number of ponds; they are more suitable for use on commercial trout farms. It goes without saying that in time there will be automatic feeders especially designed for small rearing units but at present the pendulum feeder is the most suitable for use in smaller establishments. Opinions differ amongst fish farmers about just how useful they are, but we at Two Lakes wouldn't be without them. Now, if a man feeds all the trout in the stewponds at Two Lakes with pellets, the hours he spends in one day on this particular job at the present rate of pay, cost three pounds in wages. One pendulum feeder costs eighteen pounds to buy. I bought six several years ago and they are all of them still in use, so it is not necessary to buy a new pendulum feeder each year. The daily filling of the feeders costs, in wages, one pound, so two pounds are saved. Therefore the original cost of these feeders had been recovered many times over.

Vermin

Finally we must discuss, if only briefly, those creatures who want to share in your fishery without paying, and can be classified as vermin. The most destructive of these is a creature called Man, further classified as 'poacher'. In many other languages the word for 'poacher' is much more explicit: roughly translated it means fish thief or game thief. And that is what they are, one of the shabbiest of thieves. To glorify these people by publishing books about their plunderings, which often involve physical injury to the keepers, is beyond my understanding. I know of a small angling club which is made up of men from a factory, who, in their spare time cleared out a derelict pond and a small feeder stream, and created by their hard work a wonderful little fishery. Not only had they given their time to create this fishery, they had also provided the money for stocking and for other expenses. In their enthusiasm they spoke to other people about the good fishing they enjoyed, and a number of poachers, most likely the local layabouts, heard about it and proceeded to net the pond and the stream. Of course, the fishing was ruined. Restocking costs money, and the club had to start saving up so more fish could be put into the water. Presumably those romantic souls who 'walk by night' would, in good time, treat themselves to another netting spree. And then write a book about it.

If a fishery does not employ a full-time keeper, or if there is no fishery manager, then protection becomes a problem. Frequent visits at varying times of the day and night are of some help. One club had very good results by offering the people living in nearby houses a money reward for reporting poachers. Every such householder was given a telephone number, so if any suspicious-looking characters were seen near the river a phone call could be made to the club who would send someone down to deal with the situation. If a successful prosecution resulted, the householder received a reward.

Nevertheless, even if a keeper lives on the fishery he needs additional protection, because poachers rarely come singly. At Two Lakes we have had two Alsatians in residence for years. The poaching fraternity have had some uncomfortable encounters with these dogs and, according to rumour, Two Lakes has a reputation for indulging in unfair practices! We cultivate our bad reputation, and we never walk around the fishery by day or night without being accompanied by our unfair practices. Some fisheries employ other breeds of dog as guard dogs, but though brave and intelligent, they cannot match the Alsatian, whose fierce reputation acts as a deterrent. Not even the Doberman has such a reputation.

At this point it is as well to clear up one matter. Many keepers, because of that horrendous reputation of the Alsatian, are afraid to have them living in their homes because of the supposed danger to their own families, especially small children. Any dog's behaviour depends entirely on how it is treated, particularly by children. If children tease or are cruel to an animal, and this does happen, sadly, all too frequently, the animal will bite. Any Alsatian introduced to his new home as a puppy or young dog, and treated firmly, fairly and with affection, is loyal to the death, and utterly reliable. We have had several Alsatians over the years, and have known some quite fierce Alsatians. None of them would ever have hurt a member of their own family. Moreover, their protective instincts encircle the children, and in some cases you cannot even touch the children because the Alsatian fears you may harm them. According to our experience Alsatians would never bite their owners. Indeed, when, in the past, ours have had to be treated by a vet, invariably we held the biting machine because we know before the vet is bitten we would be bitten, and they would never bite us.

A further protection is afforded by pressure mats camouflaged with turf or soil and set at strategic points. They transmit a signal to the keeper's cottage when somebody treads on them. This signal lights up the number of that particular mat, so the keeper knows in what part of the fishery poachers are active and can act accordingly. As time goes by, there are likely to be still more ingenious inventions, and we must try them all with the hope that the poaching problem can be solved.

Animal vermin also take their toll in fisheries, but they are not as destructive as their human counterparts. Years ago the otter could become quite a nuisance in a fishery but nowadays their numbers are so diminished that it is only on very rare occasions that they do harm. For instance, if an otter should find a stew-pond of trout, it would probably kill the lot. In 1948, when Two Lakes became a fishery, otters visited us regularly. At that time there were no houses close to the lakes and the otters were not shy at all, and could be seen even in daylight. Some authorities state that otters prefer eels to any other fish and will never touch a trout so long as there are eels to feed on. We found this not to be so at Two Lakes which was initially a coarse fish fishery with only a few trout introduced as an experimental stocking. The otters, always single animals, as we observed through binoculars, took any sort of fish although at the time there were eels aplenty in the lakes. I would say that an otter cannot afford to be too choosy: the hunting otter will catch and eat whatever is at hand, be it fish, eel or waterfowl. It is highly dangerous to use the words 'always' and 'never' on the subject of animal behaviour.

These days, a danger greater than otters are mink. They have escaped from mink farms and have learned to live again in the wild as did their forefathers. According to experienced keepers, mink are not a great danger to fish in wide, deep rivers or deep ponds and lakes. But small, shallow streams and stewponds full of fish can be devastated by them. From Sweden there have come reports that the fish population of certain shallow streams has been decimated by these little killers. The odd mink, however, so long as it does not get into a fish farm or stewpond won't do much harm though if it meets a partner and they start a family on the premises, the battle is on. So don't be too easy going. Remember when you see one relatively harmless little mink what can happen, and remember also that you are required to report any appearance of mink to the Ministry of Agriculture, Fisheries and Food.

Shooting the mink will be ineffective and besides, few water keepers always carry a gun with them, and when they do happen to have a gun you can be sure that no mink will show a whisker. Not that mink know about guns, it's just the luck of the draw. So instead of firearms try cage traps. These save a lot of the keeper's time, and if the traps are set in the right places, mink are relatively easily caught because they are such nosey parkers. One keeper I know has caught several mink in a trap set underneath a small wooden shed, of all places. Mink like to inspect dark places, presumably in pursuit of rats. Yet another keeper has a mink trap underneath a pile of firewood, the trap can easily be pushed underneath the wood and pulled out again if it has an occupant. Hedges, hollow trees, a culvert, underneath a plank bridge over a ditch, all are good sites for mink traps. It must be well camouflaged and baited with an egg, fish, or a piece of meat. Some trappers recommend using mink droppings in the trap: the theory is that a mink, especially if it is the resident one, will have to investigate this evidence of a visitor and will enter the trap to do so. If you want to trap mink, experiment with all these possibilities and then use the one that has shown the best results. By the way, the correct setting of traps is hard to describe satisfactorily in writing; it is worth while for an inexperienced person to ask an experienced keeper in the neighbourhood to come to the fishery and show him how to do it.

Another formidable enemy on a sport fishery or fish farm is the heron. In some countries their number is still quite considerable, although here they are not so numerous. If you want to take the ultimate action against herons, make sure that shooting is permitted. In some countries they are partially protected, and can only be shot on fisheries and fish farms where they manifestly do harm.

Shooting herons is more easily said than done. They are shy birds, and even when a keeper thinks he has hidden himself effectively, the herons will notice the slightest movement. Trapping should be prohibited. I can remember my young days, when keepers set spring traps in shallow water: a cruel and devilish method, and even if the law does not forbid such a thing, in all conscience, it should not be used. Discourage the heron, harass him and remember he is bothered by even a distant sight of you, so show yourself frequently, at odd hours and he will take himself off. If you put up a scarecrow, for a time at least the heron will be discouraged, and if your scarecrow is convincingly manlike, so much the better. You will have to put it in a different place every second or third day, otherwise it soon becomes part of the scenery. Birds and animals always notice something different in a landscape; they are very conservative and frightened by change.

Once I tried hanging sheets of newspaper on branches near the water, and for a few days the herons gave them a wide berth. I didn't alter the position of the papers, as it seemed that the birds had gone for good to fish the waters of one of my competitors. However, after a week or so, the herons were back and fishing so close to the sheets of newspaper that I suspected them of reading them or at least looking at the pictures. It was very evident that the newspaper, like the scarecrows, had to be shifted about to go on being useful.

The use of those 'bangs' used by market gardeners for keeping birds off their crops, work well against herons. The only drawback is the cost, which is high. If, as in the case of the market gardener, the cost can be levelled out over the value of the produce protected, it is well worth the money. Equally so it would be economic on a fish farm. But in an angling water the cost would be out of proportion.

Then, of course, you can criss-cross strong nylon string under water in shallow stretches. When the herons are wading they touch it, and it must be very frightening for them because I have found that they avoid such places like the plague, and for a very long time. Putting the nylon entanglement into the water takes quite some time, and you will become entangled yourself while you do it. If your wife is helping, you are pretty well bound to have a stimulating row! A more serious disadvantage, perhaps is the annoyance to the fishermen who hate any obstruction, and if the entanglements are in stewponds they interfere with netting. So it's all rather impractical unless restricted to areas where only herons operate.

If stewponds are completely fenced, even covered, with netting wire, they are completely protected from herons – and from kingfishers, as well, although these enchanting little birds get underneath the wire and then trust to your softheartedness and appreciation of beauty to let them go free when they are caught. In fisheries close to the coast, where gulls are frequent visitors, netting wire over the stews is almost a necessity and well worth the expense.

There are many other enemies who are always trying to snatch a square meal. Most coarse fish fisheries should be able to afford the loss of a few fish, because the more densely populated by man the world becomes, the less room there will be for animals and birds. Coarse fish fisheries, which in most cases are run on natural rather than artificial lines, with the fish reproducing without man's help, can even find some fish-eating predators beneficial. Coarse fish fisheries are mostly overstocked, especially with smaller fish, to the detriment of good sport. So if herons and gulls take some fish it will be in line with the balance of nature.

However, in a put and take trout fishery a policy towards predators of live and let live can be damaging. Here, any fish-eating creature must be discouraged from the very beginning. All animals and birds are creatures of habit, and if they succeed a few times with their thieving, they will come back again and again. Unfortunately, in most cases the only solution to the problem is to kill the creature. Consequently, it is wise to keep a careful watch for the first signs of intrusion, and to frighten the intruder away, before it has discovered the flesh-pots. Most of us are animal lovers, but very few animals are mankind lovers, most hate the sight of us and fear us. We have to make use of this detestation when we are dealing with vermin. It is platitude time: prevention is better than cure.

6 Management of a Small Trout Lake Fishery

Still water has become the inevitable haven for trout, whose demands are more exacting than those of most other species. They have lost river after river to the cause of human progress. The trout's new home is the large reservoir, where man, who is so careless of other creatures, stores water for his own use. We allow these reservoirs to be stocked with fish – mostly trout – but this is not done to provide the fish with a pollution free environment. Our reasons are purely selfish. We fishermen are delighted to make use of a new sort of trout fishing, and the people who run the reservoirs are pleased with the additional income.

To be fair, nearly all small lake fisheries are created for practical purposes. The water is not often used as drinking water, but more usually to supply irrigation schemes. There are some small lake fisheries built entirely for the purpose of providing fishing for clubs or private owners. Again, the object is not primarily conservation, it is profitable business. The trout may enjoy a brief life in the healthy waters of a lake, but one day they will take a fly, and then they will have fulfilled their purpose.

How can we obtain the best sport from a given area of water? The primary consideration is to make the lake habitable for all species of fish, and this includes trout for whom the water must be cool and well-oxygenated. In fact, if trout are to thrive they should not really be expected to live in water with a temperature of more than about 21°C. They can tolerate a rise of temperature above 21°C for short periods, but if the period is prolonged, especially if the temperature rises above 25°C, they will die – first the brown trout and then the rainbows, who will manage to survive a little longer. You can avoid the danger of high water temperatures by making your lake deep. The depth around the drainage sluice, the monk, should be at least three metres and a few additional metres is an advantage. The lake bottom then rises slowly towards the inflow to a depth of a few centimetres, and in these shallows all sorts of weed will grow, giving shelter to the fish and creating areas for a large number of underwater creatures, which are fish food in their turn. The deep, weed-free parts of the lake provide cooler areas into which the fish can retreat on hot summer days, and a refuge for the fish during cold winters when there is thick ice on the lake.

If your lake is a long established one, but not more than two metres in depth, it can be dredged to a greater depth. But don't dredge holes haphazardly all over the bottom of the lake. Try to make sure that the bottom of the lake slopes towards the deepest part as you excavate. This will help if you should wish to net the lake in future years. If there is no drainage system and you have the possibility of installing a monk, do so now. But never forget that the monk must always be situated in the deepest part of the lake near the dam.

Weed

People who have built a lake are tempted to plant a selection of underwater weeds. I feel this temptation should be resisted, even though a lake without weed looks barren, and you may wonder where the fish will find shelter, where the small creatures the fish feed on will live, and what about the oxygen that the weed brings into the water?

I have constructed lakes which could only be called large holes full of water dug out of the clay. There was not a single water-weed to be seen. Trout can live in these conditions, as the water itself takes in oxygen through its surface contact with the air, and through the action of the wind. And, anyway, the weedless state does not last long; in most such lakes the first small patches of weed appeared after a few weeks and during the first year there was modest growth. The second year more weed was in evidence. If a particular species of weed finds a lake with all the right conditions for prolific growth, a weed problem can develop in the third or fourth year of the life of the new lake. I have known milfoil to choke a new lake in its third year of existence, and this without the weed having been deliberately introduced.

It probably came in from the tiny feeder stream, or bits of weed may have been brought in by water fowl. So there is no need to plant weed in your new lake; things are so organized by nature that you will soon have to spend a lot of time and money on getting rid of the weed so that the lake will be fishable again!

As any area of agricultural land must be farmed to give good results, so has the whole area of a smaller lake to be keepered. Heavy weed growth can be checked in many ways. Spraying with chemical weed killers is one of the most convenient, but it is not cheap. We have experimented with some of these chemical weed killers at Two Lakes and found that they did not affect the fish, nor the small animal life in the water. However, their effect on some weeds has only been partial, though Canada weed was completely destroyed by the sprays, for one season at least. Unfortunately, it appeared again in subsequent years. However, research continues and we can reasonably hope for more effective products to come on to the market.

A number of clubs and private owners are strongly opposed to the use of any sprays whatsoever. They maintain that even if the chemicals show favourable results and are said to be harmless, the long-term effects are unknown. Most manufacturers, of course, deny that there will be any undesirable long-term effects but it must be up to the fishery to decide whether or not chemicals are used. At Two Lakes they are used in conjunction with other methods since the eradication of Canada weed by chemical sprays demonstrated how much quicker they are than any other method.

Getting rid of Canada weed by cutting with a scythe is quite hopeless for it is brittle and breaks easily into little bits. Every scrap of weed that is not collected and removed will drift into another part of the lake and start another quick growing patch of weed. A suitable spray kills the lot and so prevents future colonization.

At Two Lakes we have an anti-weed device, which is great fun to operate. It is a large wooden raft, anchored on long ropes so that it can be moved back and forth over a given area. You stand on the raft and lower a long-handled rake down to the bottom of the lake, and then twist the head of the rake around the roots of the water weed; then you pull up the bunch of weed, twisting the rake handle slowly. If you are lucky, you get your bunch of weed on to the raft and then you can slowly pull up a satisfactory rope of twisted weed. Your raft is moving slowly as you pull, and you can manage to haul in quite long strands. If you pull the raft back to where you started you can clear an area quite efficiently. As the weed is pulled up on to the raft, many of the creatures living in the weed let go and swim away. The fish soon learn what the raft means, and they assemble around the scene of activity, gobbling up the bonanza of easy food that has been disturbed. Not all the creepy-crawlies are panicked into running away, some hold tight and fetch up in the pile of weed on the raft. We always left our raft full of weed by the bank of the lake overnight so that the creatures could make good their escape during the hours of darkness and they generally manage to find their way back to the water.

This raft method enables the management to clear selected parts of the lake. From the fisherman's point of view it provides nice open patches for playing a trout which has taken a fly cast close to a weed bed. It is also the greatest fun for everyone interested in creepy-crawlies for all sorts of strange creatures can be found among the weeds.

In the 1930s, I spent several years in Scandinavia, and saw there for the first time a very ingenious method of weed control. The owner of a lake had built a very large wooden platform which was secured on to some very thick logs: this floating monstrosity measured about 25 metres square. Wherever it was anchored it excluded the light from the water and all the underwater weed died. After four or five weeks, the Swede pulled the huge raft into the next position where again the weed was quietly and efficiently and completely killed off.

With this in mind, I later developed at Two Lakes the polythene sheet method of weed control. (A large wooden platform would have been better, and I must say I would have loved to have had one, but the price of timber was prohibitive.) The polythene sheets, which are large and black, are the same kind that farmers use for covering hay and straw ricks. There are different sizes, and different gauges, but at Two Lakes we found that those measuring 16 metres by 8 metres were the largest that we could handle easily. As for the gauge, it is best to get the polythene as thick as possible. Three or four of these sheets put side by side can kill enough weed to make a useful area for fishing.

The sheets can be handled only on a windless day. They should be unfolded only sufficiently to extend their full length close to the water on the bank. Then two men each take a corner of the sheet and slide it into the water. They must pull away from one another in order to give the sheet tension so that it slides easily into the water a few centimetres underneath the surface. The sheet must always be completely submerged as it is seen to be in the photograph facing page 160. If it is not submerged, the wind will get below it and rip the sheet to ribbons. The four corners must be weighted down with bricks, or they can be tied to stakes driven into the lake bottom.

When I use these sheets I find that they kill off most weed in four weeks, after which time they can be moved to another location though the roots of the weed will still be alive and the plants will reappear the following year. If you leave the sheets in the same position for about three months, however, the roots will die off too and I have found that for three and even four years those areas which have been covered remain weed-free.

Once again, to calculate the cost, a comparison is possible: a black polythene sheet of 16 metres by 8 metres of a thick gauge costs, at the time of writing, what a man would cost for a day's work. But no man, however skilful, could clear in one day a patch of weed in an area measuring 16 metres by 8 metres in two metres of water. It is quite impossible to remove every single bit of weed from this area, and a few forgotten plants will very quickly grow again to a large clump. A black polythene sheet excludes the light completely, and every scrap of weed beneath it dies off, with nothing forgotten. You will find, when the sheet is removed, that around the weedless patch the surrounding weed bed grows like a wall to exactly the place where the sheet lay. It looks as though it has been trimmed with a knife.

Some fisheries have tried stretching the sheet on a large wooden frame before sinking it a few centimetres beneath the water surface to prevent the wind from catching it. This will only work where there are no swans or geese, because if a large bird steps on to the platform of polythene it will break through.

On the other hand, if the sheet is fitted loosely by being secured only at the corners, it will sag under the weight of the bird without breaking.

Polythene sheets have been used successfully in rivers. Here they have to be placed very carefully so that the current washes over them, but doesn't dislodge them.

In many small trout lake fisheries, it has been found that weed control is the second largest expense in the running costs. Understandably, all sorts of ideas have been tried out to find the cheapest method. As we have seen, a man wading into the water and cutting the weed with a scythe is not very efficient and is not cheap either as the wages that must be paid are high for the amount of work that can be accomplished. Furthermore, although in a river the cut weed is moved away by the current and can be guided to the banks by the flow of the river, in still water it remains where it was cut and there is the additional labour of moving it to the water's edge. If you were to leave large amounts of cut weed in a lake the result would almost certainly be that the water would become seriously deoxygenated, especially in warm weather. It needs only one very warm summer night, just before dawn when the oxygen level is at its lowest, for the whole stock of trout in the lake to die. This has been known to happen and several thousands of pounds worth of fish have been lost.

When a lake extends to twenty hectares or more, weed-cutting machines are a good investment. In a small lake, however, an old dodge can be used: try keeping some weed-eating ducks. From the great family of ducks, there are only two species which can really be called weed-eaters: the widgeon (*Anas penelope*) and the red crested pochard (*Netta rufina*), though even they, eat some animal food, (just as other species eat weed on occasion), and therefore compete for food with the fish population. However, they eat mostly weed and when they find what they like – for they have their preferences – they can demolish huge amounts of it. When Two Lakes was first being developed as a fishery, the upper lake, which is nearly two hectares, was overgrown completely with floating pond weed. Three widgeon, two drakes and a duck, devoured during one summer all the floating leaves and destroyed the root stock in the lake bottom so that the weed did not grow again the following summer. The ducks cost nothing but an equal amount of weed would have been very difficult and expensive to remove any other way.

Of course, you cannot tell the ducks which water plants they should eat and which they should not eat. At Two Lakes we had a watercress bed as a shrimp and snail breeding farm, from which snails and shrimps were collected regularly and put into the lakes to help keep the fish in good condition. One day some red crested pochards discovered the watercress bed and had a field-day. We fenced the bed to keep them out and because they were pinioned birds the fence was not very high. They found ways to get through it, ruined the watercress and had all the shrimps and snails as well. We forgave them because as a whole, they did a good job as keepers. However, before long, the fishermen themselves made the use of ducks for weed control quite impossible.

At the beginning of the season all the fishermen had been asked never to feed the ducks, because they were not pets, but had a keepering job to perform. For a few weeks everything went as planned and everybody admired the ducks for working so hard at eating the weed. But then the anglers, especially their wives, could not resist feeding the ducks now and then because they were such enchanting little things. They were quickly degraded to scrounging mendicants, and could not be bothered to eat weed. The moment a fisherman appeared at the lake side, they made a beeline towards him and begged for titbits. It became so bad that the fishermen themselves began to complain because they interfered with the fishing. They were continually having a go at the fisherman's dry flies, and there were frequent commotions what with duck catching and fly removing, ducks quacking and anglers swearing. We had to remove the ducks, and ship them off to non-fishing waters; if only the fishermen had not interfered, they would have been admirable underkeepers.

Ducks are not the only weed-eating underkeepers. Latterly, many countries have had good results with Asian grass carp to control the weed. At the moment, grass carp cannot be imported into this country, because experiments are being carried out by the Ministry of Agriculture and Fisheries to determine their suitability to our waters. The results of these tests are eagerly awaited by the Two Lakes fishery for weed control is one of our heaviest expenses and reports from European countries

above Between 25% and 40% of the surface area of a river should hold weed. In shallow water weed can be cut with a scythe.

right Thc general public use rivers and lakes as a convenient dumping ground for rubbish. Before the fishing season commences, keepers must remove all obstacles.

left Where the soil is suitable, stewponds can merely be excavated and require no waterproofing of any kind. But in sandy soils, stewponds must be of concrete or any other waterproof material.

below The same pond as above a few years later. The vegetation camouflages all concrete work and the ponds look natural.

indicate that the use of grass carp can bring the cost of weed control down considerably.

Since angling clubs in Britain have no practical experience of these fish, I asked an angling club in the Ruhr district of Germany to tell me of their experiences. Here is a translation of their letter:

'*Our lake has about twelve hectares. Years ago this lake was overgrown completely with weed and we could not fish. We tried to fight the underwater weed with chemicals but had no success. The lake has an average depth of four metres, and in some places it is deeper. The weed was one solid mass from the bottom to the surface.*

'*In 1966 we bought 600 grass carp from a dealer who had imported them from Hungary. Their size was 10–15 cm. We were flabbergasted by the results because already one year later, that is in 1967, we had no weed left in the lakes. And in 1968 and 1969 our grass carp had nothing to eat. From then onwards we began to catch them when we were fishing for other coarse fish. They took floating bread crust, worm and also potato. Their average weight is around 10 pounds. And now I will answer your particular questions:*

(*1*) *Grass carp get along quite well with other species.*
(*2*) *The other species are: trout, pike, carp, tench, perch, roach, eel and of course the grass carp.*
(*3*) *Losses on grass carp were 20 from the original 600.*
(*4*) *The grass carp is an excellent fighter when hooked.*
(*5*) *It is much stronger and fights harder than the common carp.*

'*Of course you will ask what trout and pike are doing in the same lake. Here is the explanation: we had a disease among our tench a few years ago, and lost great numbers of them, and at the same time we did not have many trout in the water, so our Committee decided to stock with a thousand small pike which would deal with the diseased tench. This the pike have done very well indeed. Our stock of tench is now very healthy and they have an average weight of 2 pounds.*'

After reading this letter I found I wasn't quite clear about what happened to the shrimp and snails and other creepy-crawlies that needed the weed which had now been eaten, so I wrote again. The Secretary of the club was kind enough to send me a second letter:

'*I wrote in my last letter that our grass carp, since 1968–69 have had nothing to eat. But that is not quite a true picture. They had eaten all the* underwater weed. *But our lake has great reed beds and these were the next item the grass carp went for. When we were happily and very quietly sitting and watching our float, suddenly one of the long reed stems was drawn underneath the water, and the roots tipped over and came floating up. A grass carp was busy, and after it had eaten the reed, it ate the roots as well. And now we no longer have any reed beds. Here again answers to your further questions:*

(1) So long as we had underwater weed, definitely grass carp were never caught by fishermen.

(2) When they had demolished the underwater weed all members of the club reported catching them.

(3) You further ask whether, when the weed was eaten, this did not reduce the underwater life. With this question you have hit the nail on the head: it was a great mistake on our part to have put 600 grass carp in our lake. In this we had been incorrectly advised by the experts. These experts were of the opinion that even 600 grass carp, in view of our tremendous weed growth, would never eat enough plants to upset the biological balance of the lake. We have now emptied our lake, and we have found that all the other species of fish have not had enough to eat and were not in good condition. And looking at our empty lake we could not see the slightest trace of weed. When we again flood our lake, and should we again have a weed problem, we will then be at great pains to stock not more than 100 grass carp.'

I have had similar letters from angling clubs in other European countries and the conclusion drawn about grass carp as a weed controller is that initially it is better to understock with these fish. Then, if the results are not satisfactory, the stocking rate should be gradually increased.

The correct proportion of weed growth in a lake should be about 40% weed and 60% weed free of the total area. In practice this means that those parts which should be weed free are: around casting platforms, along most stretches of the banks, around the overflow and around the inflow. These are places chosen not only by fly fishermen, but also are favourite places for the coarse fish angler. Should boat fishing be allowed, then great areas in the middle of the lake must be weed-free as well. In the deeper parts of the water, three or four metres, there will probably be no weed, particularly if the water is not very clear.

Mud

In a newly built lake there will be no mud problem although, as a matter of fact, two or three cm of mud actually improves a lake bottom of sand or clay. Should a lake, long-established and with a thick layer of mud, be taken over and developed as a fishery, the mud ought to be removed. Some of the suggestions made in the chapter on River Management are applicable to mud removal in lakes. But suction pumps and machines are expensive to hire, and obviously it will be more difficult and therefore more expensive to work an area which has considerable width rather than an area which is comparatively narrow, such as a stretch of river. There is an exciting new machine called the Mudcat. It is very large and requires ample space for access to a site but once it has arrived, it gets to work and sucks up the mud at an astonishing rate, and can clear and rejuvenate a silted up lake. Of course it is not cheap to buy, nor to hire, but if the money is available it is worth looking into the matter.

Should it be possible to drain the lake and expose the mud to air and weather, as described in the chapter about lake building, the natural elements will do the work for you free of charge.

Stocking

With the lake full of water and the underwater weed well under control, the next step is to see that there are enough swimming, crawling, burrowing and floating creatures to feed the fish. As a water, game or coarse fishing, is a dismal place without the varied freshwater fauna, a separate chapter has been written about these, in which we will try to give as much information about those animals which are useful to a fishery and what means are available to us to increase their numbers. Even if it has been decided that the trout are to be fed artificially, there must still be natural food in the lake. This may seem an obvious point, but it needs stressing. For instance, I used to buy some of my trout for stocking Two Lakes from a trout farm which is situated on a small river. This river supplied enough water to keep the trout farm going but was very poor in underwater life. This meant that the trout in the stew-ponds rarely saw a shrimp or a nymph. It was food pellets all day and every day, and nothing else. The trout from this farm gave poor sport to the fishermen for the first few weeks after they had been stocked at Two Lakes. They were simply not interested in the artificial flies presented to them, and it was only after a few weeks, when they had learned in the waters at Two Lakes what a natural nymph or dun or spinner was, that they started to take the artificials and to give sport.

At the same time, I bought another lot of trout from a fish farm situated on a famous chalk stream in the South of England. These trout were invariably first class risers and provided excellent sport. I visited this second trout farm several times and I noticed that if there was plenty of fly on the river a few metres away from the stews, and the trout were rising consistently in the river, the trout in the stew ponds were also gobbling up the insects. The manager told me that if there was a heavy fall of spinners the trout in the main river rose very well, but the trout in the stewponds were really boiling. Of course, the fly diet did not put any significant weight on the stew fish, that was accomplished by the pellet feeding, but every fish in the stews had learned to feed on fly.

This story demonstrates not only an obvious point, but also that it is a good idea, when buying trout, to have some information of the conditions of the trout farm from which they come. Without living creatures in the water, the best in fly fishing cannot be achieved. A large tank filled with barren water and with a few trout swimming round in it may give a man a chance to catch a trout if he flogs long and hard enough, but makes very dull fishing.

Even in a fishery that is quite unashamedly put and take, where the average fish is not expected to survive the fishermen's attentions for more than a week or so, the whole pattern of the fishing will change if the water is alive with aquatic creatures.

To conclude: you should adopt your stocking programme to

allow for the likely eating habits of the trout if they come from a farm such as I first mentioned. It would also be a good idea to stock these trout well before the fishing season opens in order that they have the opportunity of studying entomology!

Another decision that the fishery manager must make is whether to stock with rainbow trout, or brown trout, or both. Of course, he will be influenced by the club members or by other anglers most likely to fish his waters. When these opinions are being considered, they must always be balanced against the running costs of the club. If the budget is tight, rainbows are better because they are cheaper. Nevertheless, if the club does not demand quick results and the members are satisfied with smaller fish, brown trout can be stocked. Many river fisheries prefer brown trout because rainbow trout are reputed to be great wanderers and may move on and be lost in the fishery, though I have heard from many river managers that the vanishing act of the rainbows occurs less often now than it did forty or fifty years ago. I have noticed this myself. I can remember that, at Two Lakes, nearly thirty years ago, we often used to see shoals of rainbows swimming back and forth, in front of the fenced off overflow, trying to get out. But for some years now we have not seen them behave in this manner. The explanation must lie in the following fragment of fishing history.

In the 1880s the first rainbow trout that were introduced into Europe (so far as can verified) were shasta rainbow trout, a non-migratory rainbow trout. As always, when something new swims into view, there was great interest and a heavy demand for rainbow trout eggs. In order to fulfil these orders, the exporters, because they did not have enough shasta rainbow trout eggs, stripped steelhead rainbow trout, a migratory fish, so as to make up numbers. The deception may not have been deliberate because so little was known at that time about the rainbow trout and to the exporters a rainbow trout was a rainbow trout. When the European trout farms sold rainbow trout for restocking fishing waters, these rainbows with pronounced steelhead migratory instincts vanished from the waters, much to everyone's chagrin. The trout farmers now noticed that there were differences in the appearance of rainbow trout, differences which related to their behaviour. The steelhead is a longish fish and heavily spotted above and below the lateral line, while the shasta is shorter, more thickset and sparsely spotted, generally with no spots at all below the lateral line. In latter years, many trout farms have favoured the shasta type when they are stripping their rainbows, in order to counteract the migratory tendencies of the steelhead rainbow trout. In all that I have just related the constant repetition of rainbow trout may be rather irritating. I have done this deliberately to avoid confusion.

So the argument against rainbows – that they may try to escape – becomes less persuasive, and should not deter any fishery from stocking with these fish. In fact, many fisheries would give poor results if they had no rainbow trout in their waters, though in Europe it is taking us a long time to overcome the prejudice against them. Fortunately, the younger generation of anglers has an open mind and accepts rainbows as a fine sporting fish, which rises freely, fights strongly and when landed provides a delicious meal. I do not think it will ever oust the brown trout completely – and this would be sad if it happened. In very lightly fished waters, the brown trout has pride of place. The rainbow trout, being a hardier fish and having a much faster growth rate than that of the brown trout, will be the bread-and-butter fish of most angling waters, especially in put-and-take waters.

In the early days of Two Lakes I stocked with fifty per cent brown trout and fifty per cent rainbow trout. After many years of fishing I would say that there has been little difference between the two in providing sport. There were periods during midday of hot days when rainbows were caught, but few brownies. However, during the evening rise both were caught. It is unwise to listen to what the anglers have to say, because they change their minds so easily: I had one fisherman who was a brown trout addict but he soon changed his mind after an exciting struggle with a heavy, perfectly conditioned rainbow trout.

In Britain I have heard it said quite often that the rainbow trout drives away the brown trout, because it is so dominating and aggressive. According to reports from some fisheries, such as one in Jugoslavia, quite the opposite is the case. There the brown trout was the troublesome one, and as a result the rainbows, being more peacable, left stretches where there were brown trout to find other homes. Both persuasions are wrong and both persuasions are right.

The obvious answer is that where conditions suit the rainbow trout, it stays, but if everything is not to its liking it leaves. The presence of native brown trout is probably irrelevant. For quite some time now, at Two Lakes, we have observed no signs of 'racial discrimination' between brownies and rainbows. True, we have seen a rainbow chase off a brownie, and the other way about, but this fairly common behaviour had nothing of race riots about it. The explanation may lie in territorial behaviour. In some waters, even the wandering rainbows make a home and repel all trespassers. I have heard many instances of such territorial behaviour, and my own experience supports it.

One spring I stocked Two Lakes with yearling rainbows. One of these little fish took up position under a plank bridge near the outflow of the upper lake. This strong, thick plank was forty cm wide. Every time someone walked across the plank the little trout shot out from underneath and into the lake. When the footsteps died away, back came the trout and again took up its position. After a few weeks it became accustomed to people crossing the bridge and didn't move away. The fishing season passed and all through the winter the little fish lived underneath the plank. During the close season the only people using it were my helpers, my wife and myself, and of course our two Alsatian dogs. We used to greet the fish as we passed.

During the following summer the fish was observed by many anglers and its growth rate was noted with great interest. Winter passed and another summer and the rainbow trout was a well-established personality. When the water became low in the summer, and was shallow beneath the plank, the fish sometimes fed a few yards out into the upper lake. But it always returned. It had grown quite big, was very aggressive, and drove away all other trout, brown or rainbow. It was now a three-year-old, and during the next winter it vanished for a few weeks; we feared that a visiting otter had killed it. But in February it was back again under the plank. We assumed that it had been on the other side of the lake where the little feeder stream provided suitable gravel for spawning. We were quite sure it was the same trout because by now it could not really hide beneath the plank any more – its head stuck out of the upstream side, and its tail showed on the downstream side. I should have mentioned that, quite deliberately, we never fed the trout when it was parked in its favourite spot, because we wanted to prove to ourselves that it was the place not the perks that was the attraction. My wife had given this rainbow trout the name of 'Lonely Heart'. And on the last two Christmases before the trout's death, it received Christmas cards addressed particularly to itself: Lonely Heart, Two Lakes. What our postman must have thought of the goings on at Two Lakes! All stories such as this have a sad end, but at least this sad end is also a sporting one.

Every year at Two Lakes there are a few new rods and one of these, who had not heard about Lonely Heart, saw a nice trout rising a few metres out from the overflow to the upper lake, cast a fly and caught it – a beautiful four-pound rainbow. When the fisherman came to me in the evening to weigh in, I suspected nothing, until he told me, with great excitement, where this particular fish had been caught. Quickly I went to the plank bridge. There was no sign of Lonely Heart in his usual place or a few metres out into the lake. I had an awful feeling that our friend was gone. For a few days we kept on looking but in the end we had to accept the fact that he was gone for good. We are a rod-letting fishery, and we cannot afford to be sentimental. But, although it was a little unfair to the angler, for a long time my wife gave him dark looks.

To sum up, a fishery manager should be without prejudices, and should try stocking with both brownies and rainbows. If, after a season or two, it is found that one does better than the other, then obviously, in re-stocking he must favour the more satisfactory of the two. The correct stocking of a fishery determines the quality of the fishing, and also the price that people are prepared to pay for a ticket. Lakes, and rivers as well, which are rich in insect and animal life, can be stocked with smaller fish. If the angling pressure on such a water is light, and the trout are given time to grow, they will become splendid fish and will prove the cheapest form of stocking. But in this day and age there are less and less waters where a few rich and discriminating anglers can monopolize good angling space. Most waters, lakes and rivers, have a great number of anglers on their banks and it is not practical to stock these with small fish and then wait two or three years for them to become catchable. As I have said previously, heavy stocking with sizable rainbow trout can be backed up with stocking yearling brown trout.

The price asked for the fishing governs the number of trout an angler is entitled to catch on each visit. It also governs the average weight of the trout caught. This matter has already been touched on in the chapter on River Management. It is very misleading to give specific figures. So much depends on where you live. So look at it from a different angle. We will presume that on a season ticket the angler makes twenty-five visits and, of course, he would like to catch his limit on each occasion. Let it be remembered that it is a physical impossibility for a fishery manager to arrange that an angler catches fish on any particular day: even with freshly stocked fish, weather conditions and other factors make success uncertain. However, the stocking should be such that in three visits there should be two days on which he catches something. Let it be remembered also that it is a physical impossibility for a fishery manager to arrange for an angler to catch fish if the angler is inept. So, we can qualify: if the angler is not successful on two out of three days, the stocking policy should be such that he at least sees other people being successful. The fish must be there, and must be seen to be there.

Moreover, the average weight must be taken into consideration with the number of fish caught. A fishery with a two pound average weight and a total catch of one thousand fish would not necessarily be more expensive than a fishery with a one pound average weight and a total catch of two thousand fish. But a fishery with a two pound average weight and a total of two thousand fish, that is a different matter. As the number of fish per angler and the average weight increase, so the price must rise accordingly.

I think the management of a put and take fishery should aim to have between 100–150 trout per hectare. It has been found that if the number of trout diminishes to between 30–50 trout per hectare, it takes a lot of hard fishing to find the fish, and it is high time to restock in order to bring the number of trout back again to something like 150 per hectare.

When management wants to stock a lake with small fish, much depends on the quality of the water. The best lakes in lowland areas have given an additional annual growth of up to 200 kg per hectare. The poorest additional annual growth in small mountain lakes came to only 12 kg per hectare. This annual growth was obtained on natural food without any artificial feeding whatsoever. A lake with an additional annual growth rate of 200 kg per hectare could be stocked with 800–1600 yearlings per hectare. A poor lake providing only 12 kg per hectare should be stocked with less than 100 yearlings per hectare. The fishery manager must arrive at the stocking rate for his lake by checking on the natural food in the water.

Recently I was looking through a game fishing periodical. Three pages were crammed with advertisements from river and lake fisheries, offering day tickets or season tickets. The great majority were asking prices which were laughably low. The prices would scarcely cover the running costs, let alone stocking. Even the most unbusinesslike of anglers has now begun to realize that in fishing if you don't pay much, you don't get much. And looking at the names of the fisheries it is easy to see that they are always losing their rods as the same people advertise year after year. Some people just never learn!

Fishing may be a hobby for the fisherman, but for the man who runs a fishery it is a business, and he must never forget it. It doesn't matter if it is a private or a club fishery – no business flourishes unless it gives value for money. An obsession with buying the cheapest and providing the cheapest indicates only that the fishery manager does not understand his job. As an instance, take the buying of stock fish. At the time of writing, the price list of a trout farm in the South of England quote the price of £25 per hundred for rainbow trout of about 20 cm in length and £60 per hundred for rainbow trout of about 30 cm. On this particular farm, rainbows are hatched in December–January, and in the following autumn, when their first year of life is still not complete, they have grown to an average of 20 cm. In normal winter weather it takes until the end of March to grow to 30 cm. With good feeding many of these fish, three or four months later in July, can weigh 1 kg, and the quickest growers amongst them can weigh considerably more.

Now, the fishery manager who understands about the rate of growth of rainbows, and is not obsessed by the idea of buying the cheapest, will buy the right trout at the right time. If he should decide to buy 20 cm trout in March, because they are relatively cheap at £25 per hundred, he has made a mistake. The greater proportion of these last year's yearlings, as they would be, will have reached 30 cm on this trout farm. Only the slow growers, the runts, will be 20 cm or less in March. With the best care and plenty of food, even, these will never make 1 kg in summer. They are what is called in farming circles 'bad doers'. When you are buying trout, it is best to buy the largest sizes according to the time of year. Then there is always the possibility that trout which are 30 cm in March are not last year's yearlings, fourteen or fifteen months old, but rather they are slow growers from previous years. It is important to buy the stock fish from a trout farm with a good reputation, where the trout farmer will state the age of the fish.

These slow-growing fish have their uses. When they are offered at a low price they can be stocked in put and take fisheries which have a low average weight. Mind you, they will compare unfavourably in looks with the fast grown silvery young fish, but you get what you pay for. If the fishing ticket is modestly priced nobody can complain if the trout are not well shaped and are patently cheap.

Keeping the Lake in Good Trim

So, you have a lake of healthy water, the right proportion of weed and mud, and the sizes of trout which you think are right for your purpose. Now you must see that the lake is fishable. Often, on smaller lakes, fishing from a boat is not allowed. But the banks are bramble-infested, there are thickets of alder and willow and though the surroundings make a bird watcher's paradise, the poor fisherman has nowhere to cast. The banks must be cleared, with a few patches of alder and willow left here and there otherwise the place looks artificial and park-like. There must also be some reed beds.

Should woodland, on one side of the lake, extend right down to the waterside, don't cut the trees to make casting possible. On days when the wind is strong, it is very useful to have these sheltered areas where the fly can dance over the water and the trout rise to them. You can make your heavily wooded banks fishable by building wooden or earthen piers out into the lake. These should be about fifteen metres in length in order to prevent the fishermen from catching the branches with their back casts. It is not advisable to build a bridge-like structure resting on stakes driven into the bottom of the lake. In the first place, they would have to be very wide and very well secured so that the fishermen feel safe. Many older fishermen do not like to step on such constructions even when they are quite solid. Secondly, when a fish is being played and decides to circle one of the stakes or dart below the platform, in most cases the fish will be lost.

At Two Lakes we have several of these piers, and nearly every year the winter gales blow down some trees which we salvage and have cut into manageable sizes for use in building new piers or repairing established ones. Two rows of stakes are driven 1½ metres apart and parallel for about 15 metres out into the lake. Then the timber is piled up between the two rows of stakes until it is 10–20 cm above water level. Everything is then covered with a mat of small sticks, which mustn't be more than about 14 cm long or they trip people up. Finally everything is covered with soil, or turf or garden weeds. These wooden piers need attention every year. Something is always going wrong with them, and they have to be repaired *before* the fishing season opens because it is very awkward carrying out repairs when the things are in use. Moreover, it always happens that if a pier is being repaired, that is the one the fishermen are determined to fish from. I have even known them to barge in and fish right beside the wretched man who is trying to carry out the repair! Piers, therefore, made of earth, rather like small peninsulars, are much less trouble. At Two Lakes we have several of these as well. A small bulldozer pushed them out in less than a day, and they last for ever with hardly any maintenance at all, though grass must be cut and brambles and bushes discouraged from growing on them. With an established lake, finding soil to push out may prove an insurmountable difficulty. At Two Lakes we have compromised by making earthen piers wherever possible and solid wooden piers everywhere else.

If you propose to build fishing piers, you must think as an angler does when positioning them. Of course, as I have said before, there must be some parts of the lake that no fisherman can cover with his fly, where the fish can take sanctuary, and there are always a few places where casting is almost impossible and only the high priests among fishermen can succeed. So do not site your pier where casting is difficult anyway. A fishing pier in the right place can be an ideal spot for Mr Average and never forget that in both a rod letting fishery and a club you have to provide sport for Mr Average.

If an angler is casting to a trout way out in the lake, he can stand upright but if he is fishing for a fish nearby, it is better for him to keep out of the fish's 'window'. Here management can help by letting grass or reeds grow knee-high around the nose of the fishing pier to provide cover.

I have said elsewhere that you must keep paths clear so that the fishermen can move about the fishery without having to fight their way through a jungle. But although the paths must be kept clear, grasses, rushes and low vegetation must be left at the water's edge to provide camouflage for the fishermen. Place some little seats at favourite fishing spots. They need not be elaborate. In fact, if you have at hand some portions of sawn-off tree trunks, they will do admirably.

In a river, dead and dying fish are swept away from the fishery by the current but this doesn't happen in a lake and the corpse of a fish, floating with its white tummy up, catches everyone's eye. A dying fish too lies on the surface of the water eloquently advertising the fact that it is dying. The fish has been hooked and lost, and is injured, sometimes its mouth is so injured that it cannot eat so it takes a long time dying. But the fisherman has only to see one corpse and immediately the cry of 'Disease!' goes up. Furthermore you will have the fisherman telling you that he never sees a dead fish in a river, so there must be something seriously wrong with your lake. The answer is to copy nature, and as the river removes by its action the dead fish, so do you. Go out in your boat and collect any corpses in the early morning before the fishermen appear. If you put out these dead fish, lightly covered with soil and out of smelling range of the fishery, you will be very popular with the local fox population.

In bitterly cold winters when thick ice forms, lakes with a muddy bottom often suffer a high winter kill of fish. To overcome this danger, divert a strong flow of water into the lake and out again, if this is possible. This will bring in freshly oxygenated water and remove dangerous gasses which develop in the mud and cannot escape into the air because of the ice cover. Alternatively, let off a few centimetres of water from the lake through the monk so that there is a small air space beneath the ice. Of course, this applies only to small sheets of water.

When the water level is lowered on larger areas, the ice will collapse, and through the cracks in the ice, gasses can escape and fresh air can enter.

When poaching and vandalism are discussed, it is not unusual for a fisherman to suggest that your lake may be poisoned. Don't be alarmed. Poisoning a lake isn't easy. In a river the current will distribute the poison, and great damage can be done. But in still water, as we know from our own attempts with Derris powder, it is a long and laborious chore to distribute the stuff effectively. Vandals have neither the time nor the equipment to poison a lake completely, though of course, a quantity of poison thrown into a lake will do damage locally.

As well as all the thought, work and care that a manager must expend if he wants a successful fishery, he must be able to set the tone, to create the right atmosphere. Management and fishermen are not on the same side of the fence and they never can be, but there need be no bad feeling. The odd black sheep may stir things up occasionally, but it is up to the manager to spot the danger signs and deal with the situation, just as he must be alert to spot the danger signs and deal with the situation in the actual running of the fishery.

7 Management of Coarse Fish Fisheries

The manager of a trout fishery has an easy job in comparison with the manager of a coarse fish fishery. He has to consider only one species, the trout, whereas the manager of a coarse fish fishery has to cope with the varying demands and characteristics of a number of different species. The variables are habitat, diet, predation and conditions and seasons for spawning. The successful manager must be able to deal with such questions as whether or not to stock and what with, when to reduce the numbers of a particular species, what size limits to set, what catches to allow, and how to keep age groups in proportion. If he were to feed all these problems into a suitably programmed computer it would probably blow up!

Actually, the precepts for coexistence amongst different species are age-old. In the wild every river and lake is cropped. Surplus fish are harvested, and such predators as the otter, the mink, the heron, the cormorant, grebe, pike and perch are the harvesters, and an admirable job they make of preserving the balance of nature, that newest plaything of our time. In eastern Europe the latest development is for man to do the cropping, substituting for the natural predators whose ranks have been depleted there, just as they have been here. But cropping, such as taking home the catch of coarse fish, is unacceptable in Britain, for the moment at least. Indeed, we insist on all catches being returned to the water even though they will add to the congestion by breeding, as will their progeny after them. As you may have guessed, I am *not* a return-them-alive advocate.

To support my opinion let me give you an example that I have often used with our fishery management students – the tench production at Two Lakes. It works like this. Every third year we empty our lakes in rotation, that is to say we do not empty them all at the same time. All the water is drained away through the monk system and most of the fish are caught; the few that are left are sufficient to start off the new tench population. Male tench become sexually mature in three years, and the females in four (except for a few who may mature a year earlier), so you can see it is necessary to empty the lakes not later than every third year.

The tench which we have caught, many thousands of them, are in good condition and have a ready market and their numbers correspond well to the acreage of water available. Two Lakes consists of eight sheets of water and occasionally it has been impossible to empty a lake at the appropriate time. Sometimes as many as five or six years have passed and then of course, we have found a multitude of tench. Some of these have been quite large but the bulk have been small and all were thin. If we knew the exact number of cubic metres of water in that particular lake we could prove beyond doubt that there were several tench to each cubic metre of water. With that density of tench population it is unbelievable that any nymph, snail or shrimp or other food animal could survive, let alone breed to increase its own population. If we were to leave the lake unemptied for yet another two or three years, the tench would become stunted. Unfortunately, there are many coarse fish waters which are in a state similar to this: teeming with quantities of small stunted fish.

Pike

Now I can visualize a posse of put-them-back-alive anglers jumping up from their seats and shouting, 'Put in pike, they'll soon restore the balance!' I wish it were that easy. The trouble is the pike have not read the right books and therefore don't know that they must take only small fish. They have an unfortunate habit of taking whatever comes along. Given the choice of two fish swimming into its reach it will grab the two pound tench or roach and not the fingerling which is accompanying the larger fish. If the waters in question are small, and the pike spawn successfully, the stocking of pike will eventually result in very few other fish being left on the premises, just a small number of small hungry pike and a brace of large ones who had eaten up everybody else.

But, if an angling water is several hectares in extent and has a great number of fish of non-predator species and if it has, moreover, no contrivances for emptying, then it is very suitable for the use of pike as croppers. The only snag is that precautions must be taken to prevent the pike population from increasing too much, and the pike from becoming too big.

If you let a pike grow into the monster class, say to fifteen or twenty kilos, it will be damaging to the fishery because many large fish of other species will be caught by it. It is your job to hold the balance between the pike and the other species, which isn't easy but can be done.

The pike, for instance, can be shot. There are still some keepers who do this. In rivers the shooting is year round, but in lakes only the spawning season offers opportunities because at that time of year, March and April, many pike are close to the banks and in shallow water. Of course, shooting is noisy and attracts attention and when you are close to a built-up area it can be dangerous.

Two other methods which are still quite popular with river keepers are snagging and wiring. These are more easily done in rivers than in lakes, but are time consuming and not so productive as intelligent trapping. As for trapping, it is very effective. Some fish, carp for instance, won't enter a trap readily, but pike will. In rivers these traps must be set so that their entrance points downstream. In lakes the traps must be placed not too far away from the bank. A long, narrow, open space between weed beds is ideal. The traps work all year round, and never need to be baited. Some manufacturers use wire netting for the outer covering, but many keepers insist that traps covered with nylon netting catch better. Further, it is as well to use traps with wide wings on both sides of the entrance in order to guide the fish into prison (see Figure 30).

Netting pike is another worthwhile method, most successful during spawning time because the shallows in the lake are easily encircled. So long as weeds and reeds are not an impediment, there can be good catches. Electric fishing on the other hand, is an effective method of removing pike and other unwanted fish from a small river but is not satisfactory in lakes, especially when they are deep: netting is better.

Then there is control by the prevention of successful spawning. Pike require shallow water, ditches, flooded meadows, weedy

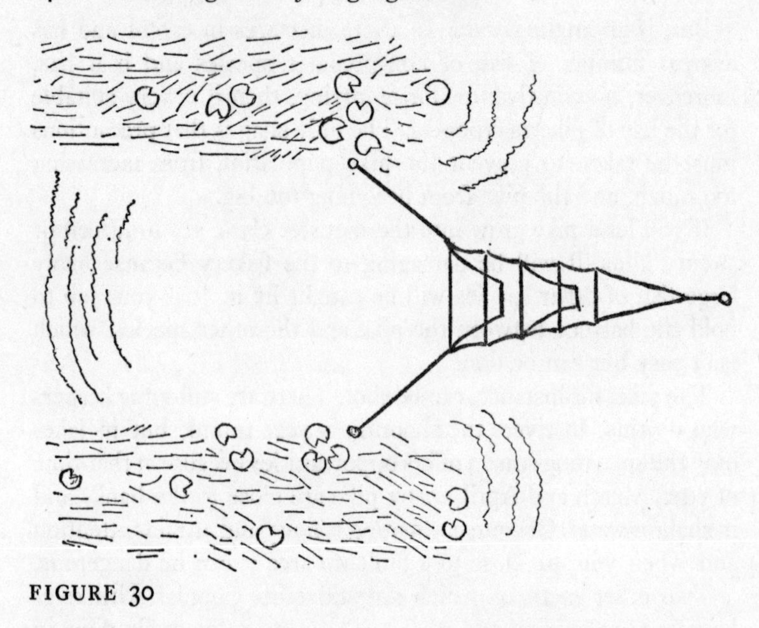

FIGURE 30

areas for spawning. So if your fishery should be a gravel pit which has no such areas, or if it is very deep, the pike may not spawn at all, or if they do the results will not be very successful.

As young pike live in shallow, weedy areas they are prey to herons and kingfishers as well as to other predatory fish, including their own tribe. Natural enemies keep down the numbers of small pike and man can give a helping hand with the large ones. Angling clubs on the Continent permit their anglers to take away the larger pike that they catch, although the number is limited. On the Continent, of course, pike are eaten.

The East European angling clubs with the far-sighted policy of combining food production with angling, even go so far as to stock with pike every season. It may be of interest to give figures about stocking, if only as a guide. Remember that much depends on the individual waters. When I sifted through the reports of success and failure at the various clubs, it soon became obvious that the smaller the fish stocked, the greater the losses. This did not apply only to pike, it held good for carp, tench, trout and all the rest.

In lakes the stocking works out at 1000–1500 pike fry per hectare, with subsequent losses which may go as high as 90–95%. When stocking fingerlings 15–20 per hectare are sufficient. Should the young pike be introduced into a lake with a very large population of stunted roach, rudd, or crucian carp, then you can venture to put in fifty fingerling pike per hectare.

Some of these clubs tried a rather novel stratagem. They stocked with large pike of one sex only. This meant that they knew exactly the total number of pike in their fishing water, and could allow the pike to crop without any interference. From the few fisheries where this idea was tried out, the reports were rather disappointing. The rules of the club did not permit anglers to fish deliberately for pike, and besides the fishery's interests were centred on other species. Even so, the pike were hooked now and then and if they were injured they had to be killed. They proved to be well-conditioned fish, all of those which were killed, but much to everybody's disappointment autopsies showed that most of the fish eaten by these large pike were large fish. There were very few small fish. So the purpose of introducing the pike, to reduce the population of small fish, was not fulfilled, and to add to the disappointment, the fish the pike ate were those fish which the anglers themselves wanted to catch.

Trout, Chub and Eel

There are several other species of fish you could use for fish population control such as the trout, chub, eel, perch and zander. It is a mistake to put trout into a coarse fish fishery just for the purpose of their eating coarse fish fry. It is a different matter when the trout in a trout fishery take coarse fish fry, as in such waters the trout is the primary fish and the management concentrates all its efforts on improving its lot. But in a coarse fish fishery the trout would not be a satisfactory helper. All the anglers are much more interested in the coarse fish so when the trout are hooked, as they often are, they are roughly handled and flung back into the water. So it is that most of the trout become thin, ailing fish, feeding very little on the coarse fish fry, till one day they will tip over and die. The trout which can adapt themselves and become expert fry catchers and angler avoiders are few and far between and prove how useless the whole operation is.

The various coarse fish have their preferences. The chub, for instance, likes running water and is not happy in still-water. They also tend to eat fish only when they are older, so as population controllers they have a limited use. So too the eel. In some waters they feed voraciously on small fish, as do trout, but in other waters not at all. All eels, however, eat quantities of eggs during the spring and early summer when the coarse fish spawn and in this way they could contribute to controlling the number of coarse fish. Furthermore, eels are in competition with other fish in that they eat the small food animals that other fish feed upon. However, in most coarse fish angling clubs there are some members who have a fancy for eel fishing, and like to take their catch home to make a good meal themselves.

In each fishery the manager or the stocking committee must decide whether or not eels should be encouraged in their waters. If the answer is thumbs down, you will find an elver trap very useful though it will not be able to keep the eels out entirely. (For a description of an elver trap see page 51.)

In most coarse fish fisheries, particularly on the Continent, the eel is very welcome indeed. So much so that if enough eels don't enter the fishery of their own accord, or the anglers take away too many eels, the waters are actually restocked with elvers. If stocking, it is not advisable to put in eels which are longer than 30 cm, because these larger eels are older, and may be close to the time when they will migrate downstream to the far-distant Sargasso Sea. Moreover, these larger eels have probably been sorted and may contain a high proportion of males which do not grow so fast as the females and therefore remain smaller, and of less interest to the angler.

It is best, therefore, to stock with elvers in the spring as the ones caught at this time of year along the British, Dutch, German and Danish coasts run to about 3500 elvers per kilo. If they are bought from further south, from, say, France, Portugal or Spain, the average is about 2800 per kilo because there has been less weight loss. Such elvers can be stocked at about 100 per hectare on a yearly basis.

It will take time to determine accurate figures from results of stocking, so the above figure is an estimation. It is better to understock than to overstock. I read of one angling club which had very good results from a stocking of 100 elvers per hectare. The club then decided to increase the stocking rate to 500 elvers per hectare. In the following seasons although more eels were caught than previously, they were small and the anglers soon started to grumble. The average weight was considerably less than it had been in the years when only 100 per hectare were stocked. Of course, the club stocking committee promptly returned to the original stocking rate. Obviously, the food in the lake could not support a larger population of eels.

It is useless for smaller clubs on rivers to stock with elvers, because most of the fish will depart far upstream. They will also enter side streams, ditches, ponds and lakes. If a particular river system has a very small elver run and stocking is required, this can be carried out only by the Water Authority or by a large fishing association of that particular river system.

Perch and Zander

The next on our list of predators to be considered is the perch. If this smartly dressed pirate is wisely used it can be a great help in keeping down the smaller fish. But from the outset the perch population must be managed very carefully. It starts with spawning. The perch female, in common with many other fish females, lays an enormous quantity of eggs. One female in a smallish lake is quite capable of producing all the young perch needed to replace the generation which came before, but only if all the eggs hatch. A lot of eggs get eaten and parasites and fungus also take their toll. We humans complicate the situation and upset nature's arrangements when we step in and create a condition which is favourable to one species or another.

Perch find many angling waters to their liking and multiply at such a rate that their own tribe, as well as other species, are prevented from growing large. When perch are small they are in direct competition with all the other fish. Perch of under about 15–20 cm in size eat plankton, insect larvae, shrimp and all other small underwater animals. If the number of perch is such that very few of them grow to the size at which they become fish eaters, then the perch population can satisfy only the tiddler snatchers, and (a more serious consequence) they make a tiddler ground of the whole angling water. Therefore, every large perch must be returned carefully to the water and the small perch removed. You should try to build up a good number running to one kilo or more in weight. Older, larger perch, in contrast with pike, do not take large fish.

To return to the perch's egg laying habits. They deposit their eggs in ribbons on weed, timber, stones, sometimes more than one metre long and varying in width from 2–5 cm. Because of this you can attempt the first perch population control, by constructing bundles of brushwood (see Figure 31) and placing

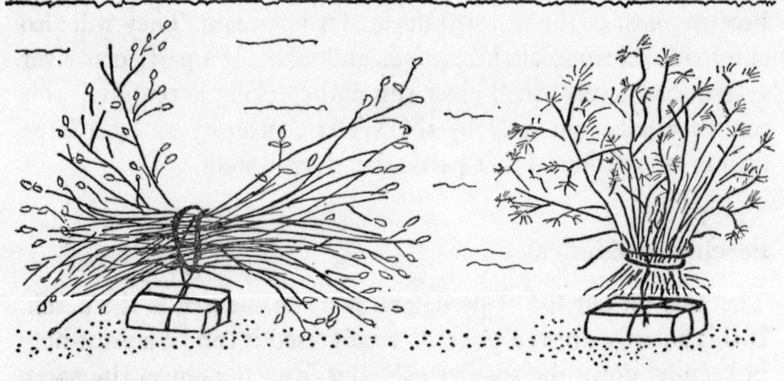

FIGURE 31

them not too far from the bank in the water every 25 to 30 metres. The bundles must be sunk so that at least 50 cm of water is above them. Perch must like such brushwood bundles because they have been observed swimming back and forth above them during spawning. When spawning is finished, the bundles must be fished out of the water and destroyed. They cannot be used a second year because by then the twigs will be far too brittle and the bundle would break to bits. This egg collecting should not be delayed because, with changes in the water temperature, the eggs may hatch unexpectedly soon.

When you consider that a perch female weighing half a pound can lay up to 30,000 eggs, you can appreciate that destroying the eggs makes considerable inroads on the perch population. Of course, some perch have rejected your bundles of brushwood and have laid their eggs, undetected, on other underwater objects or on weed. These eggs will hatch into quite a number of perch, but because of the keeper's efforts the density of the young perch population will be less and all the survivors will find better growing conditions.

Curiously enough, after they have left the egg, young perch

are more vulnerable than other fish at the same stage of development. Nearly all baby fish, after absorbing their yolk sac, swim to the surface, gulp a mouthful of air and press it into their air bladder. They only do this once or twice, but the tiny perch, (they are about 5 mm long) behave differently. With unbelievable energy they come to the surface of the water again and again. They pause on some weed at the bottom of the water, and then up they come again. They are unable yet to swim horizontally. This behaviour continues for some days and they become easy prey to any creature on the lookout for a meal.

Moreover, this swimming pattern is the reason why young perch find difficulty in remaining in running water. If the parent fish have spawned in a river, and the young perch after hatching commence their up and down swimming performance, the slightest current will carry the little fellows downstream. Some will land in quiet backwaters and survive to help sustain the perch population in the stream. But should a dam be built across the stream forming a lake or a reservoir, the current would be slowed and would give the tiny perch a greater chance of survival, and in many cases a perch population explosion will occur.

The manager of a club or the stocking committee have a difficult task in convincing their club members that perch of roughly over 20 cm must be left alone, or that if they are hooked, the fish must be returned unharmed to the water. The larger perch not only eat the smaller fish of other species, but also eat their own kind. It is a very unwise policy to permit the large perch to be removed from the water in order to give the younger, smaller ones a chance to grow. The result of such a policy would be that year after year new generations of perch, non-fish eating perch, would be added to the angling water and the average size of the perch would become smaller and smaller. Unfortunately, many of the fish would be sexually mature.

Research has shown that the growth of perch to the fish-eating stage is slow, but when this is reached, at 15–20 cm, their annual growth rates increase considerably. In order to put on one kilo in weight, the fish has to eat about four or five kilos of other fish. When the perch have reached this stage in their development the fishing water becomes a very worthwhile perch fishery.

But the development of the worthwhile perch fishery involves the problem of weed cutting. If there is an over-abundance of weed, all the small fish including the small perch can escape from the predators into the thick protective cover. Consequently, the larger perch are forced to seek other animals, such as insects, for food, and will put on growth very slowly. Weed beds should not be too dense and should have large open spaces around them. In this open water larger perch hunt together and are able to surprise shoals of smaller fish which are feeding on the plankton in open water.

Fishery managers prefer their lakes and rivers to have smooth, obstacle-free bottoms to make netting easier. Perch prefer just the opposite conditions. They like the small ridges, you could even call them hills, such as are found on the bottom of clay or sand or gravel pits, which make the greatest perch fisheries.

A pike's hunting habit is to lurk in a hiding-place waiting for some fish to swim by so that it can rush forward and catch it unawares. Perch hunt quite differently. They swim in groups and when they come upon smaller fish they chase their prey. Some observers hold that perch will surround a shoal of fish and then dash amongst the panicking crowd. The perch is a free roving hunter and prefers some localities to others. The underwater hills which I have just described are often covered with weed, but are prominent like an underwater island in the weedless deep water around. Of course, these weed covered hills become hiding-places for many smaller fish and the hunting perch patrol around them (see Figure 32). It is a good thing if the manager of the fishery knows of such places and can advise the anglers of them.

The management of the large rush and reed beds in a lake

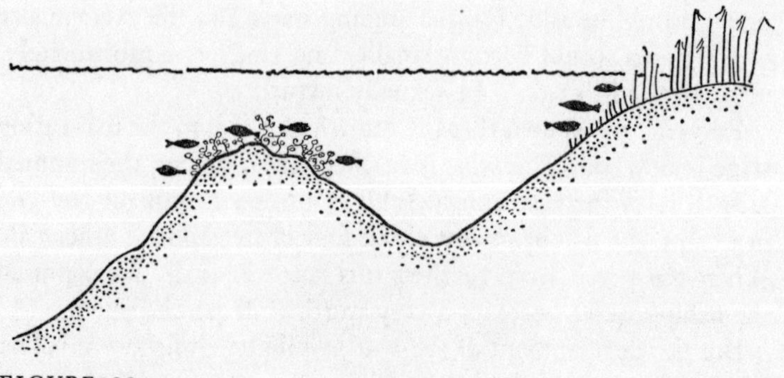

FIGURE 32

affects the perch population, as it does other fish, and will be discussed later.

And so we come to the zander which is another fish useful in keeping down the number of small fish in a fishery. The zander, or the pike-perch, as it is called in Britain, takes only smaller fish, as does the perch. Even in large zander, when an autopsy has been made, you do not find fish of more than about 200 g. The mouth of the zander is smaller than that of the pike.

The pike-perch's original home was Eastern Europe. From 1850 onwards this fish was deliberately introduced into lakes, reservoirs and rivers in Western Europe, and was finally brought into the British Isles. The first zander was stocked in eastern England, and since its arrival has extended its range. Opinions about this fish are very much divided, so it is better to take a neutral position and determine how the zander fits into the overall picture of an angling water. First of all, let us consider whether our customer, the angler, would benefit from the presence of this fish. He would find it a fine sporting fish, and if he takes his catch home, excellent to eat. The North American relative of the zander is extremely popular with fishermen on the other side of the Atlantic.

As for the environment in which the zander thrives: it prefers rivers that are deep and slow moving, and it does very well too in still waters with a hard gravel bottom, where there are wide open sheets of water, plenty of plankton and little weed. The food of the zander fry is predominantly plankton, and if a lake is so rich in plankton that the water takes on a cloudy appearance, then the zander will put on a lot of growth. It could be that under such ideal conditions the little fish would be the length of a finger by autumn and at this stage, *unlike young perch*, would commence taking other fish. Of course, the fish it would take would be small – the young coarse fish which the manager wants to keep down in numbers. Small fish are the zander's main food from the second year onwards and a zander population can flourish only where great numbers of small fish are present. If the number of smaller fish diminishes, then the number of zander must be reduced, and this can be done during the spawning season. Like perch, zander lay their eggs on roots and branches and also on the hard, gravelly bottom of the lake. The eggs are not produced in long ribbons as are perch eggs, but either singly or more often in bunches of varying sizes which are attached to the chosen surface. Again the heaps of brushwood are brought into use, but when you are putting them into the water, avoid any muddy places. If you have put down a good number of heaps of brush, the zander will use these as nests, and when spawning is completed, they can be taken out and destroyed. By these means, and by angling, the number of zander can be kept under control. If, on the other hand, you have no zander and want to introduce them, you can confidently stock with this species if you have a large, deep gravel pit with no pike, not too much weed and an over-population of coarse fish. About 1500–2000 fry per hectare or 150–200 fingerlings per hectare would be a reasonable stocking, and of course, you can stock with spawners with individual weights of about 2 kilos. Good results have been obtained with three such fish per hectare, two males and one female. One male and one female have given equally good results, but the extra male is an insurance in case one is sterile. These older fish should be stocked in the spring, while the younger fish can be stocked in the spring or autumn, though only in lakes. Rivers should be stocked only in the spring because the zander tends to wander less at that time of year. When they are stocked in rivers in the autumn they have been known to move very far away indeed.

As the zander is a fish which demands rather special conditions in order to thrive, efforts to stock it should be repeated only for two or three seasons, and if these attempts are not successful the whole idea should be abandoned. Generally speaking, the very first stocking will show if the zander will do well in the new location.

A final snippet of information which may be of interest even if it has nothing to do with the actual management of angling waters. Zander guard their nests very fiercely. I heard from a Hungarian zander breeder that he has been attacked several times by the fish when he tried to remove their nests. He and the members of his staff were actually bitten in the hands by furious parents.

Carp and Bream

Now we can discuss those fish which most interest the coarse fishermen. I have been in charge of a commercial coarse fish angling water, have attended meetings with coarse fish anglers, and have collected information from angling clubs both here and abroad, and all this has given me an understanding of the anglers' demands and dreams and grumbles, and their favourite fish. There are differences in outlook from country to country, some differences but not many, which is astonishing. The differences mainly concern what happens after the fish has been landed. Some anglers put everything back, while others take their catch home to provide dinner for the family. But when it comes to the favourite fish over a wide international scene, the roach comes first, closely followed by the carp. The other places in the popularity stakes are difficult to assign, so closely do the species crowd upon one another.

Instead of the roach, let us first take the carp, because there is more information available on this fish than on any other. Moreover, the information about the carp's habits can teach us much about the habits of other coarse fish. If you want to be a really good manager of a carp water, you must first get to know something about the history of carp farming. Historians give us varying dates for the beginnings of carp farming, but it can be assumed that farming as opposed to just keeping a few carp in a pond, began in Europe somewhere between 800 and 1000 years ago – plenty of time in which to collect a valuable store of useful information.

One of the pioneer carp farmers' first discoveries was that carp spawn successfully only when the water temperature remains at 18°–19°C. The point is that carp were introduced from warmer climates into Northern Europe, and they have never adapted to colder waters, at spawning time anyway, which tends to be from the end of May into June, and sometimes even later. High water temperatures are not constant even at that time of year in Northern Europe, so carp spawn very irregularly in such countries as Britain, Holland, Belgium, Germany, Poland and Russia. Though most angling waters rely on their carp stock for restocking, it is only those which are sheltered from strong winds, and where the sun's rays can reach the whole surface area of the water, that can hope for sufficient reproduction of their wild carp to keep the stocks up. There will not be overmany carp so none may be removed from the club waters.

From the carp farmer's point of view depending on luck and hope is completely uneconomic, and carp farmers have therefore developed a system which, although successful, is far too complicated to be employed by angling clubs. The clubs are better off buying their stock.

An angling club without carp in its waters may wish to stock with these fish, but they would be well advised to think carefully first. Stocking rivers with carp is not always effective, unless the river has a slow current, is wide and deep and has reed-beds protecting large bays and other quiet stretches. The sport provided in proportion to the money spent on stock fish would be disappointing, though the carp may find a few places which are to their liking and grow to quite a good size, one day to provide an angler with some memorable action. There may be the odd carp (having found its way from some lake higher up-stream, perhaps) even in stretches of river that have never been stocked. These days the Water Authorities do not look kindly on river banks which are wild and uneven: they like straight banks with fast flowing water and as little weed as possible, but the carp have different ideas (see Figure 33) and a really worthwhile carp water is likely to be a lake or a large pond.

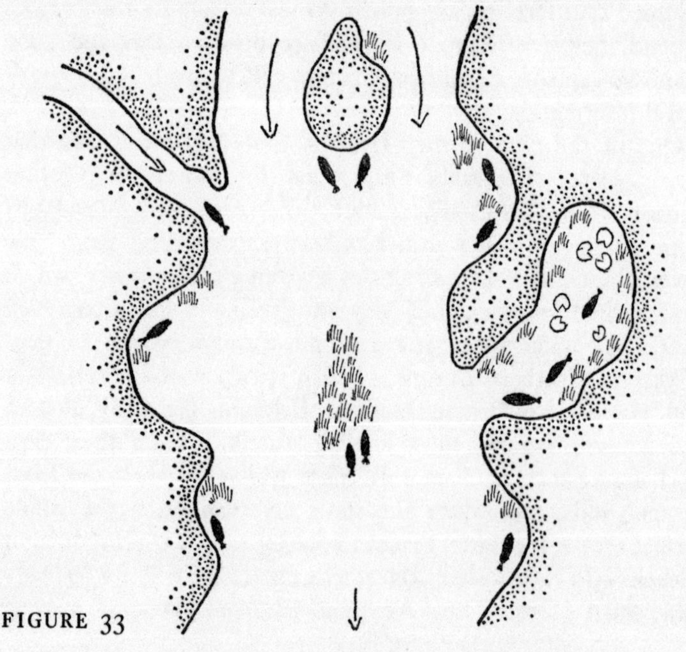

FIGURE 33

Such a lake should not be too deep, so that during the summer the water can get really warm, and the lake bottom must be soft and with some mud. I repeat, some mud, not half a metre of thick, foul-smelling ooze. It is also a great advantage if the lake can be drained every three or four years. In all probability the carp will not spawn, so the stock can be controlled.

Stocking with carp fry is very wasteful. Losses vary from lake to lake but they are often as high as 50%, and can soar to more than 90%, so you could not even estimate the number of survivors per hectare. A carp farmer drains his ponds every year and checks on the number of fish, and if your lake can be emptied, you should do the same. Experience (and not only my own) has shown that the best results are obtained by stocking with one- or two-year-old carp.

Again, as with trout, the stocking figures differ considerably, particularly when you take into account the amount of food animals available for the stock of fish in your lake. If carp are the only species, stocking could be at the rate of 150–200 two-year-old carp per hectare. If yearlings are stocked these figures could be doubled. Carp must not be stocked every year if the waters contain no pike, and if the fishing rules do not permit anglers to take away the carp they have caught.

Reports from angling clubs indicate that after some years such carp lakes are not favoured by the average angler for the older and the bigger the carp become, the more difficult they are to catch. Eventually only a few dedicated carp fishermen will fish such lakes. They consider this type of fishing to be both challenging and rewarding.

Should the carp be introduced into a lake which already supports a large population of other species, then the number of two-year-old carp per hectare should not be more than twenty, unless the water holds large pike, in which case the figure could be doubled or even trebled. Furthermore, stocking should be on an annual basis. All reports show that the new carp stock is easy prey for pike. Nevertheless, the carp is a clever fish, whether considered from the point of view of the angler or the fishery manager. It is particularly important to the latter who must bear in mind that the carp, being clever, is much better at finding food than are other fish. This means that if great numbers of carp are stocked in a fishery, all other species will have less food than they had according to the previous fish/food balance. In these circumstances bream will be the first to suffer. Bream and carp like the same conditions and gather the same type of food, so in the competition the bream will be the losers, becoming thin, and in the case of small bream, failing to put on growth. Roach and tench will also feel the pinch. A further embarrassment is that merely in order to keep going a big carp needs a large quantity of food, and if it is still growing it needs still more. So a lake with a great number of larger and older carp becomes unproductive and it is important that although the figures given for stocking sound rather small, they should not be exceeded.

Once more Two Lakes provides an object lesson, this time in overstocking. When we took over Two Lakes in 1948, it was still a coarse fish fishery and, for a time, I ran it as a ticket water for coarse fish before transforming the whole fishery to a trout water. Before stocking with trout took place, the lakes were drained completely and all the coarse fish caught, counted and sold to a dealer. One two-hectare lake produced many thousands of roach, tench, bream, eel, perch, and seven hundred carp. Nearly all these carp were between one and two kilos in weight. The largest weighed three and a half kilos. Scale readings showed that the bulk were over ten years old. Very few younger ones were included in the muster, and only two baby carp, the survivors from all the spawning activities we had observed in the late and very warm spring. All the carp were themselves stunted, and must have kept down the growth of all the other species. Among the thousands of roach there were very few over 250 g. and among the many perch there were a few around the kilo mark. Later the lake was refilled and stocked with the proper proportion of trout, which thrived on the vast quantities of creepy-crawlies. Obviously the lake had been grossly overstocked with all species, and in particular with carp. Overstocking is similar to a creeping disease, destroying life and creating in its wake other ailments.

There is the myth of the wonder lake, which always crops up when management problems are under discussion. In this wonder lake, sometimes quite a small one, great numbers of carp live happily with great numbers of other species. All the fish are in perfect condition, and many are close to record weight.

Someday if we have led good lives, we may all be allowed to visit this lake!

Another myth is the age that carp can reach. In fact a carp that dies of old age is unlikely to be over thirty, though a few have been found which were forty years old, and I have heard of some as old as forty-six. The weight they can gain is not relative to their age, but to the food available. Carp from 20 to 25 kilos are often only sixteen and seventeen years old, and generally it is from about this age that they cease to gain much more weight. For the good of the fishery one should really remove the old and very large carp before they go back in condition and die. These very large fish consume great quantities of food and have collected a wealth of experience about anglers and their ways, and they become almost uncatchable.

It is almost impossible to determine the sex of young carp, and that of sexually mature carp can only be discovered just before spawning time when the female can be recognized by her girth, resulting from the great mass of eggs she is carrying. The vent of the female is round and swollen, reddish in colour and protruberant. That of the male is smaller and cleft-like, shaped like the letter Y and drawn inwards. The outer rim of the pelvic fin is bent outward in the female and the pelvic fin of the male, often smaller, is bent inward (see Figure 34).

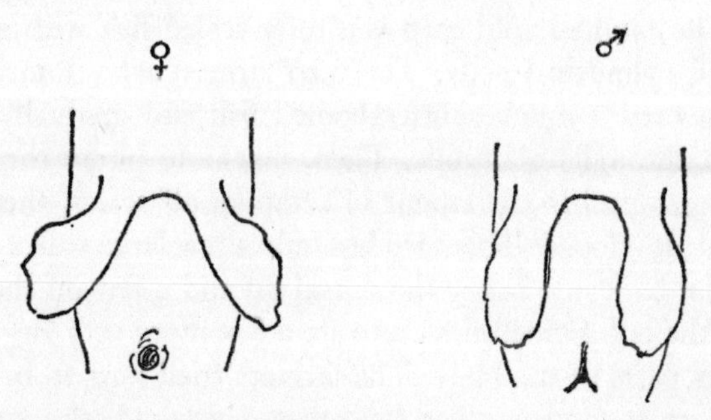

FIGURE 34

In the breeding season the males of nearly all the fish belonging to the cyprinids, the carp family, develop small wart-like tubercles on the head and gill covers, and these may extend all over the back clear to the tail. The tubercles seldom cross the lateral line. If, during the breeding season, you slide your hand over the male barbel, chub, roach, rudd, bream (this fish has very many tubercles), minnow and many other species, you feel the roughness of these wart-like growths. Female cyprinids are smooth and slippery to the touch.

To return to the question of stocking. Angling clubs in Czechoslovakia have come up with a new idea. They argue that if you have a put-and-take fishery for trout fishing you should have the same for coarse fishing. As the Czechs eat coarse fish, lakes are stocked with sizable carp, and anglers pay nothing for the day's fishing, but pay by the weight for the fish that they catch so that somebody catching an eight-kilo carp pays double that paid for a four-kilo carp. There is also a limit on the number of fish taken each day. Of course initially there was a hullabaloo in the fishing world and categorical denials of any interest in catching tame carp just stocked from a fish farm. There was a similar commotion when put-and-take trout fisheries started to operate. But everybody soon got used to the idea, and it was good from the national point of view to combine angling with food production. The idea spread to other countries, and should prove useful in the context of the imminent shortages in the world supply of food.

I said when we began discussing carp that they originated in warmer climates. In particular these warmer climates were the lower Danube and other rivers and lakes further east right into Asia. The original wild carp is a fully scaled fish with a rather long and cylindrical body. The carp farmers who domesticated this fish bred a much shorter-bodied fish and gradually distributed it throughout Europe. Then, maybe to please the housewife by saving her the labour of scraping off scales, the mirror carp was developed. This carp has only a few large scales, mostly along the back just below the dorsal fin and a few on the fleshy part of the tail. Sometimes there are a few more very large scales on other parts of the body. The farmers tried next to breed out all the scales, and another type was developed, the zeil carp. (*Zeil*, pronounced zile, means a line.) This fish usually has only one row of large scales along the lateral line, although sometimes there are two or even three rows. Finally the breeders succeeded in evolving a carp without any scales at all. This has been given many names, but is most commonly known as the leather carp. But here the fish breeders overstepped the mark. It soon became

right Using a wooden raft for weed pulling permits the precise location of weedbeds.

below Black polythene placed on top of a weed patch will kill all plant life underneath it by excluding the light, but it does not harm the fish or their food animals.

above If the first stage of netting is not carried out correctly the whole pull will be a failure. Here the man in the boat feeds the net evenly into the water so that it hangs from the floatline like a curtain.

left In the final stages of the pull, the lower line, the leadline, has been brought up first so that the fish cannot escape.

apparent that the leather carp had not the same growth rate as the scaly and mirror carp, and when disease struck, it was invariably the first to be afflicted. Often some of the leather carp's fins are deformed or missing. In short, the poor thing shows all the signs of degeneration. And it does not breed true: the offspring include scaly carp, mirror carp, and all sorts of combinations. The fishery ministries of some countries have advised carp farmers not to breed from leather carp, nor to use them for stocking angling waters. Angling clubs are well advised to follow this advice.

All the bad features of the leather carp are also found, though to a slightly lesser extent, in the zeil carp, so you are left with scaly and mirror carp for stocking purposes. And please, when stocking, deal only with those suppliers who have a good reputation. Figure 35 is an illustration of the different types of carp: scaly or common carp, mirror, zeil and leather.

Bream must be classed together with carp because in many ways they are similar in their behaviour, their environmental demands and feeding habits. I have already pointed out that the carp is cleverer than the bream, and can make living conditions difficult for it. Many good bream waters have been ruined after the introduction of carp. It so happens, however, that it works the other way about as well: the bream will spawn whereas most likely the carp will not, and the greater number of bream will not permit the carp to develop to the full. Both fish act as a brake, one upon the other.

Consequently, both species should not be in the same waters, or at least the number of carp should be kept so low that the competition for food is not felt. The number of bream can be controlled by continuously netting the surplus. A seine net with a mesh of one centimetre measured from knot to knot is the most suitable for catching out the smaller surplus fish. The experienced netters must watch the many volunteers who always appear when a netting session is on. They tend to treat the fish roughly, and pack too many into the containers which are used to transport the fish from the net to the waiting lorries. All fish suffer from clumsy treatment, particularly bream, and many will die then or a day or two later.

With respect to the predators, while pike take roach because they are present in great numbers in shallows near the bank,

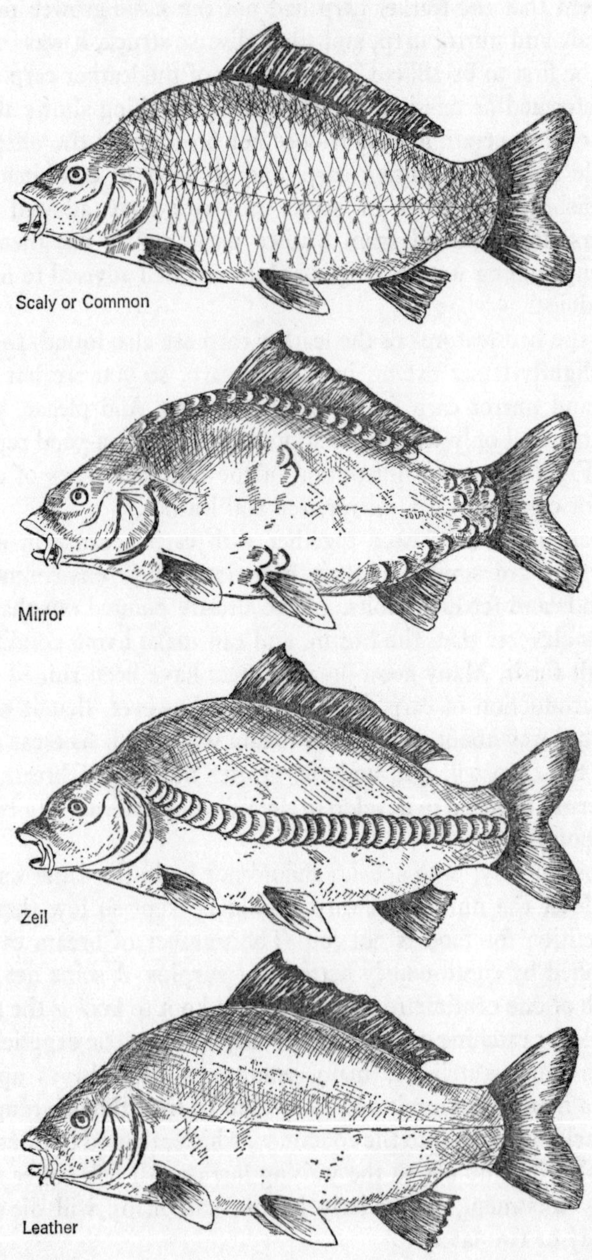

FIGURE 35

pike ravage the bream less because they live more in the open deeper water. But if zander are present, they will take great numbers of the small bream.

Roach, Rudd and Crucian Carp

Salmon and trout are the stars of the game fishing world, and both anglers and fishing writers are always digging up new items of interest about them. As to the star of the coarse fishing world, the roach anglers could have much better sport if they gave more attention to the roach's unfortunate predisposition to reproduce on the grand scale, so quickly do they overpopulate a fishing water. Sport is much more satisfactory if there is a reasonable stock of roach provided, of course, that the stock has not been kept low by disease or pollution. But too many fishing waters have such a fantastically high roach population that the individual fish rarely reaches even the half pound mark, and the rudd, crucian carp, bream and perch add their contribution of stunted fish to the hordes.

Looking through the reports from angling clubs right across Europe, there are those happy fisheries with roach averaging one pound in weight, while other clubs announce an average weight of a pathetic few grammes. How do the top roach waters produce their big fish? The most telling necessity is stock control, restricting the number of fish to the correct proportion per hectare. With any cyprinid, and of course roach in particular, you must determine whether or not the water is overstocked. There are various ways of checking, some of which are quite complicated. The simplest thing to do is to net out a good number of fish, and examine their condition.

You can tell from a quick look at the length of the fish relative to its weight whether it is in good condition. Look carefully at the backs of the fish which must be round, not thin like a knife edge. Such thinness is an indication of starvation. The undersides of the fish must be round, and when you make an autopsy, they should be full of food. The sample should contain a reasonable proportion of larger fish, and scales from these and some of the smaller fish must be taken and read. Information from scale reading should correspond and confirm other observations you have made. If the fish are not stunted and are in good condition, you can assume even though you do not know exactly the total number of fish, that the waters have roughly the correct fish population.

There is, for example, a small sheet of water, about five hectares, which has a reputation of being a good roach water, but contains rudd, tench, a few very large carp, and pike as well. Roach of over one pound are caught regularly and the two pound roach for which the fishery is famous are caught many times during each season. The angler who fishes this water for the first time is struck by the fact that there are only small numbers of younger roach. The regular anglers, however, know that there are not all that many small fish of the other species either. The carp have never spawned and are those remaining from a stocking of some years ago. Their number is less than twenty and they are very seldom caught, but are seen quite often. The tench were never numerous, because one side of the lake bottom is of hard clay with little weed, so spawning facilities were not favourable. Moreover, the environment as a whole does not suit tench. Then there are pike which come in all sizes but are not numerous. The rudd do well, but the roach are the best doers.

The population of the fish in this fishery is controlled by a large flock of very fat white ducks. On the farm beside the lake, ducks have been kept for a longer time than anybody can remember. Every day this posse of ducks patrols the shallows of the lake and any fish spawn, roach, rudd, pike, tench, and any young fish, are cleared up as though by a vacuum cleaner. The ducks grow fat and are killed off in the autumn, and then the following spring a flock of new ducklings are introduced.

In this fishery all fish caught by the anglers are put back alive, even the pike. Over the years, on two different occasions, the management committee decided to ask anglers to kill all larger pike, since the stock of big pike was beginning to build up. When the numbers of pike had been reduced, their destruction ceased.

The salient point about the stock control in this lake was that it commenced in the first year of the life of the roach. Moreover, ground baiting by the fishermen was not allowed, because it would only attract the ducks and make angling impossible, so it may well be that the lack of ground bait reduced the chances of survival for many young fish which had been overlooked by the ducks. It must be a possibility that the huge quantities of ground bait used in many fisheries are a bonanza for countless numbers of small fish.

If there is no interference from man, in most waters in their natural state, the competition for food is so great that a large proportion of the very tiny fish starve to death. This is especially so in a cool summer when zooplankton is scarce and the fry have little to eat after having absorbed their yolk sac. They can die in their thousands. The manager of a coarse fish fishery should welcome such ruthless culling and remember that nature's efforts will be thwarted by huge amounts of ground bait helping keep alive unnecessary numbers of fry.

Another famous roach water is a reservoir in Germany, so large that it houses more than one sailing club. During the fishing season there are anglers all over the place. The dominant species are roach, bream and rainbow trout. Roach of one pound upwards are plentiful. What is different about this reservoir is that commercial netsmen are licensed to operate; the Water Authority in charge of the reservoir permits the netting of roach and bream by the ton. Most of these fish go to the food markets, but the best specimens are sold for restocking other angling waters. Visiting anglers are amazed by the tonnage of the roach taken away, but their interests are looked after by the Water Authority. The staff keeps a continuous watch on the roach stock, and, if there are indications of overnetting, the permits of the netsmen allow only a smaller tonnage to be taken away the next season. This state of affairs has continued now for years and anglers have understood that only the continuous stock control by netting can give them such exceptionally fine roach fishing.

So, be it ducks, heavy netting, trapping, lowering the water level, poisoning the spawning areas, predatory fish, or whatever new methods we may discover, all must be for the purpose of keeping down the number of young fish. There will always be some who will survive all the hazards to develop into large fish.

A final example of the paramount importance of fish stock control: when a coarse fish farmer wants to bring his little fish up entirely on natural food, he puts, let us say, 30,000 ready-to-feed fry into a pond of one hectare. If the weather is kind, and there is plenty of plankton, by the autumn, they will have reached the expected size. But the fish farmer wants the fish to grow normally, and he would never contemplate letting the same number of fish per hectare remain in the pond for a second year. According to the amount of food in the water, 1000–2000 fish per hectare would be left, and if he were to keep the fish in the pond for a third year, the number would be reduced to less than 500 fish per hectare. These figures are high. Most coarse fish farmers would stock less if they were depending only on natural food. Of course, if the fish are fed additionally with artificial food the number of fish per hectare can be much higher.

It all adds up to a strong case in favour of the control of fish stocks, and particularly of roach which will spawn vigorously anywhere, from the shallow water and weed which they prefer, to a depth of several metres. Young roach frequent shallow, weedy parts of the water, as do pike, especially young pike, and when the two species are in the same waters, both do well. The pike have good meals and some roach have the chance of becoming really big because there are less relatives to eat up the available food.

Every year unknown numbers of little fish are produced, and are added to the many generations of older roach. A pond of one hectare would be grossly overstocked with 5000. But no doubt many of you have witnessed netting operations where such ponds have produced one hundred thousand of roach, most of them stunted. And often, with a fanfare of trumpets, the whole miserable lot are transferred to another already overstocked angling water to provide fresh blood! I hope soon the time will come when more practical ideas prevail and roach fishing will improve to its full potential.

Rudd are so similar to roach in their behaviour and in their demands on the environment that all that is said of roach refers to them as well. Rudd, too, can give a magnificent performance in over-populating a water very quickly. And crucian carp. Any angling club which has reasonable sport with the established roach, rudd, bream, and tench should avoid adding crucian carp as well. They multiply at such a rate that not only are the crucian carp stunted themselves, but they drag all the other fish down with them. Scale reading of crucian carp is not much help because there are often false rings during the summer growth, which makes accurate reading very difficult and can give a distorted picture of the crucian carp population as a whole.

Angling clubs in Rumania have tried a new trick in managing this species: they have stocked some of their fishing lakes with hybrids between carp and crucian carp. These hybrids are mostly male and are generally sterile. Therefore, the population, once stocked, will not increase. You can identify these crosses quite readily: they have only a thin barbel, one on each side of the mouth, and the second pair of barbels is so small that it can easily be overlooked. In carp, the barbels are distinct, while the pure crucian carp has no barbels whatsoever. These sterile hybrids provide good sport, and on an average weigh half a kilo.

Tench

Some fish show themselves flamboyantly, so that everybody has to notice them, while others are modestly retiring to the extent that there are only indications of their presence. The latter applies to tench. The first catches of most angling novices are little perch, bream, roach and crucian carp. Catching tench comes later in the fisherman's experience, though even experienced anglers sometimes maintain that a fishery doesn't hold enough tench because they happen not to have seen many. Of course, the first reaction is a demand for restocking, which may not be at all necessary. The tench may have spawned, and if they have done so successfully for one or two seasons, they will spawn again. The actual number of tench taking part is not important, because a successful outcome is dependent on such things as the weather conditions after the eggs have hatched. Indeed, the first few weeks in the life of the tench fry can be decisive in determining the future tench population.

Tench are very fussy about conditions for spawning. The lake must have sufficient shallows where the water becomes warm early in the summer, a bed which is soft and plenty of soft underwater weed. Milfoil is one of their favourite spawning plants. If the conditions are right they spawn prolifically every season. I have already mentioned the tench at Two Lakes, and I might add that there is a significant variation in the spawning success of these fish in the different lakes. The Upper lake, which is the oldest, produces a bumper crop of young every year. The other lakes vary, with Home Pool producing the least baby tench, although other ages flourish. Such a lake as this, which has no shallow areas and has a bottom of hard clay, needs stocking but, once they are introduced, the tench can grow on to an impressive size.

Tench are easier to sex than are most fish. The pelvic fins of the male are much larger than those of the female with a thicker outer rim, and often the fins are rather twisted. Furthermore, the pelvic fin extends as far as the vent in the male, but not in the female (see Figure 36). Female tench grow faster and bigger

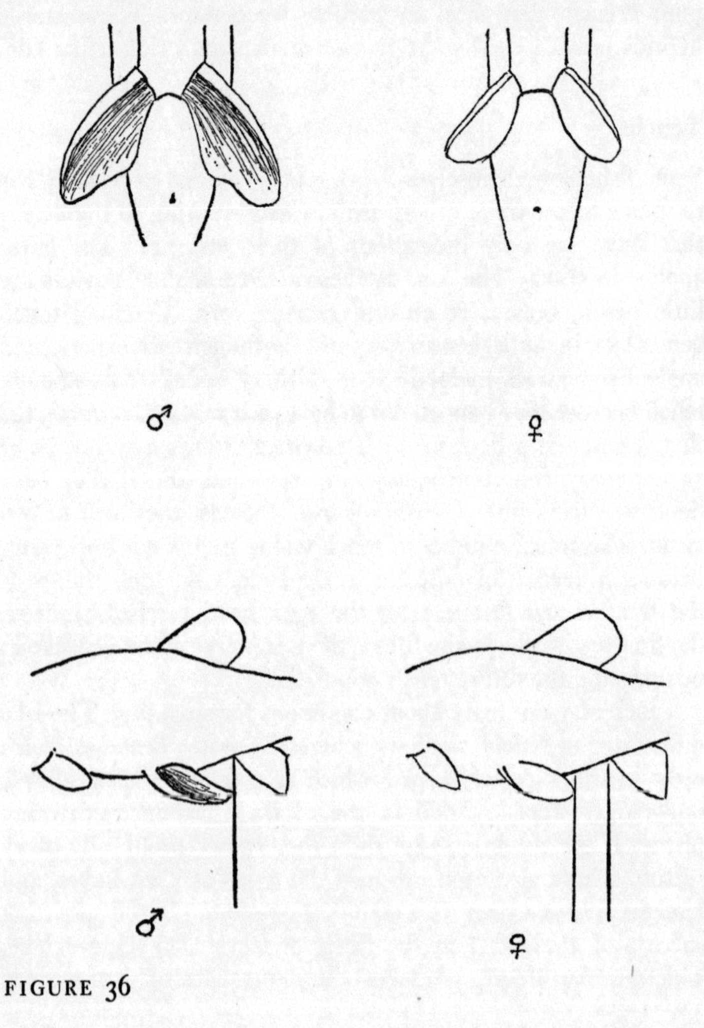

FIGURE 36

than do the males, so many angling clubs stock only with the females. The great advantage of this (aside from the fact that the fishermen catch bigger fish) is that the management knows exactly how many fish were stocked per hectare and for the succeeding few years the number of tench will vary very little. Results from stocking with females only have been reported as good. It may sound a formidable task, the sexing of a few thousand tench, but in practice it is not difficult. Our students at Two Lakes and myself have found the work easy so long as the tench were not too small. Mind you, the work must be done conscientiously. One tench incorrectly sexed can upset completely a carefully planned stocking programme.

Good tench waters often have large areas of water-lilies and, along the banks, extensive beds of rushes and reeds. These are favourite haunts of tench, although if conditions become too jungle-like even they will move out. Through thoughtful cutting, reed beds and water-lily patches can both become better holding places for tench and also gives the angler a better chance of reaching the fish. (See Figure 37.) This planned cutting benefits other species of fish as well. If it comes to the point, there are very few improvements and kinds of thoughtful work which do not benefit all species and the fishery as a whole. Poor angling results again and again have been proved to be the result of overstocking. Even tench, finicky as they are about spawning, can become over-abundant. At Two Lakes we have found that netting them out is not all that efficient; the best way is to empty the lake completely. We have always been amazed how tench endure the rigours of very little water for a sustained period of even some weeks. An astonishing example of their endurance occurred during the remodelling of Home Pool. The water was pumped out completely and a bulldozer got busy scraping the soil up onto the banks. When things had quietened down and rain had created some little pools, there were the tench in each one, bright-eyed and bushy-tailed and ready to go – their prospect of substantial growth greatly increased by the diminution in their numbers.

So there we are. We have discussed the different species of fish, some aspects of the complicated relationship of one species to another and various other matters. I know you have reached the stage where you are determined to ask me the sixty-four

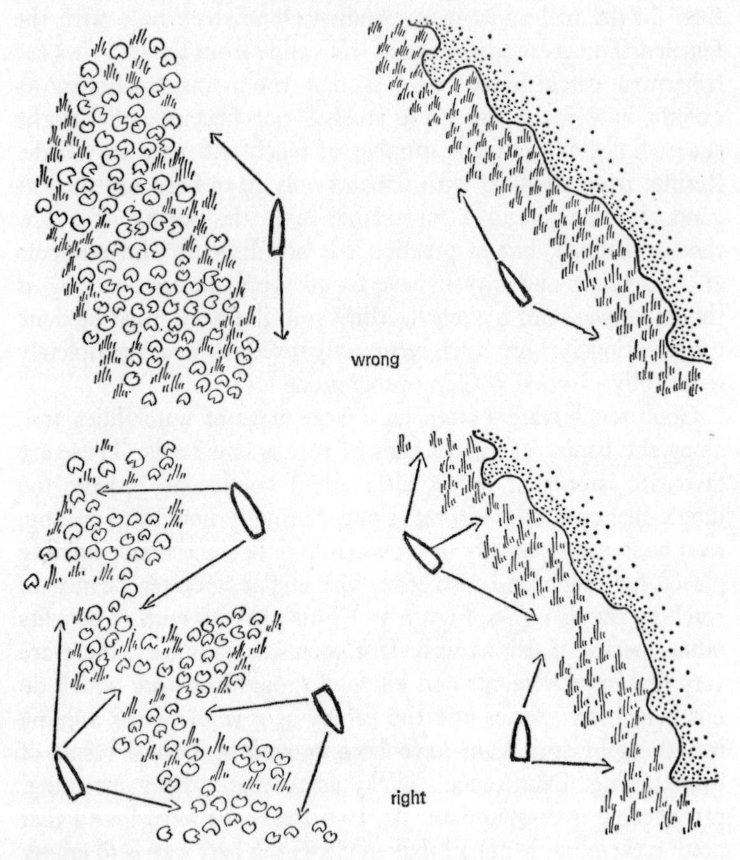

FIGURE 37

thousand dollar question: 'How in Heaven's name are we to know how to stock a mixed coarse fish fishery correctly?' This question has come up many times during discussions I have had with my colleagues in fishery management, and we have chewed it over in all its aspects.

To begin with, we have to understand that lakes can be classified into five types: very good lakes; good lakes; medium lakes; bad lakes; and very bad lakes. Very good lakes can provide, without artificial feeding, from 300 to 500 kg of additional growth per hectare. A very bad lake, and this could be an old and deep stone quarry, may provide less than 10 kg per hectare additional growth on its fish population. These figures are relative to coarse fish lakes. It is interesting to compare them with the figures for additional growth of trout per hectare, given in the Chapter 'Management of a Small Trout Lake Fishery'. Should you have a lake which is a little better than medium, and should you have been able to drain it completely, you would be in a position of complete stock control. After the lake had been refilled and left for six months without any fish, you can get on with your stocking. It will be easier if not too many species are involved. You have decided to stock only with carp, tench, perch, eel and roach. You put in twenty two-year-old carp per hectare and one hundred elvers per hectare. You buy four-year-old female tench from a reliable coarse fish farmer, a man who is telling the truth when he says they are four years old and are female, and you stock the tench at the rate of two hundred per hectare. The stock control with these three species will be easy because they will not spawn, with the exception of the carp which may spawn if the late spring and early summer are unusually hot. Next come 500 well-grown roach, average weight 250 g each, per hectare, and 100 perch of over 20 cm each, again per hectare. The lake is now understocked with fish. But after the first season the situation will alter dramatically. The roach and perch will have spawned.

As previously explained, you may collect a quantity of perch spawn to soften the blow, but the roach will hit you below the belt and produce many hundreds of thousands of offspring. The perch will do their best to help you, and even the older roach, and certainly the carp, will help by eating as many as they can of the baby roach. You have no means of knowing how many little roach will survive their first year, but with five hundred parent fish, even without trying hard, fifty thousand roach could quite easily be alive the next spring, per hectare, that is. The following year the older roach will spawn again, and the following year, and you will be in a nightmare situation. Your remedy is to get busy and net the shallows of the lake. You will want a seine net with one centimetre mesh measured from knot to knot, and continuous netting will bring down the number of small roach and perch. It is impractical to use a net with a mesh less than one centimetre because it will become too heavy for you to move it through the water. You can use a trammel net, but they are very cumbersome to work with, and have three net curtains which entangle the fish. If all the fish are to be killed this would not matter, but when the fish, at least the better ones, are earmarked for restocking, too many are damaged when they are being extricated. Trammel nets are used less and less these days, partly because of their cost and the difficulty of repairing them.

If you succeed in keeping down the small roach and perch, your lake will become a first-class angling water.

Stocking, Close Season, Size Limit

We have covered the subject of stocking and come to the conclusion that it is seldom necessary to restock coarse fishing waters. The necessity arises only when pollution or some other calamity strikes a fishery, or when a particular species is required for special reasons. The question is where to buy the fish stock.

Only fish farmers and fish dealers with the best reputation should be selected. They must give a verification *in writing* before the fish are delivered that the fish are disease-free and of a specific age, and size. If the angling club finds that the fish are not, let us say, two-year-old fish, but rather seven- or eight-year-old stunted fish, no payment should be made. The age of the fish can be determined by a sample scale reading of the consignment. Dealers of questionable honesty sometimes deliver fish so late in the day that it is already dark. You should be highly suspicious of such a delivery. There may be something wrong with the fish or the numbers may be incorrect. And never buy bargains. For instance never buy tench which are offered cheap. They may all be males, the females (which grow faster and bigger) having been sold to somebody else for a higher price.

Perch and zander, with their rough scales, should never be transported together with other fish in the same tank. When they are packed closely they injure the other fish.

Fry and yearlings should not be introduced into their new home all together in one lot. A concentration of so many little fish could at once attract many of their enemies. Introduce them in small batches into those places that they inhabit naturally.

When spawners have been bought immediately prior to the spawning season, they should be handled very carefully and released in small groups. All helpers should be reminded to handle all fish with the greatest care. The younger the fish, the more care is needed. The difference of the water temperature between the transport tanks and the lake or river should be equalized slowly. For each trip, carrying the fish from the transport tanks to the river or lake, the water in the carrying vessels must be fresh; and not too many fish should be put in at once.

All hand nets used should be of knot-free netting, as knots under pressure make deep marks in the fish's skin. Moreover there should never be too many fish in a netful.

If common sense has prevailed throughout the stocking procedure, everything should be satisfactory. But remember that if you plan to stock with fish, permission must be obtained from the Water Authority of your area.

Do we need a close season for coarse fish? Arguments for and against have been bandied about for a long, long time and generally the consensus is for a close season during the spring. The difficulty is that the spawning seasons of the various species overlap. Pike start spawning in March, while tench may still be spawning in August, so what should be the duration of the close season? It may protect the fish during their actual spawning, but it does not protect a fish full of spawn from being caught and handled, and maybe killed, a day or two before the close season commences. Alternatively, fish which have just finished spawning are weak and in poor condition, and being very hungry are more easily caught than at other times during the open season, which means that they have not been allowed a close season sufficiently long to enable them to get back into condition.

The argument, as you can see, is involved, and gives promise of becoming even more so. Perhaps the average angler does best to accept the close season as laid down by the authorities who can take a broad view, based on information from many different sources.

Another thorny question is that of the size limit. One argument in favour of the size limit is the fact that fish grow quite quickly until they are sexually mature, and at that point their growth slows down. Therefore the fish should be protected until it reaches its first spawning season. If the fish stock is to be secure, which means if there are to be plenty of fish, a great number of spawners, larger fish, must be present to produce plenty of eggs. You will not have plenty of eggs if you have taken out the fish before they are able to reproduce. Likewise, the longer the fish are left alone the more chance they have to put on weight.

Then there are arguments against size limit. For instance, in a lake the growth rate of the fish alters over the years because the productivity of the lake becomes poor. The result is that a fish of 15 cm is much older than the same size fish would have been many years previously; in short, smaller fish will spawn. Another point, if a species of fish increases very quickly, the result is that there will be a tremendous number of fish in the water, and these fish will become stunted. In these two instances alone, what purpose would be served by a size limit? Moreover, roach do not live long, so what would be the reasonable size limit for this species? On the other hand, carp, bream, catfish and a few other species live for many years, so should we protect them for a longer period and set a larger size limit? There are many more questions. I can only conclude that the decisions should be left to the appropriate authorities. The limits they set may not be ideal, but they come closer to it than do the limits suggested by individual anglers.

There is one final item in the management of coarse fish waters. If times or attitudes alter, and if here in Britain coarse fish are taken home to eat when they are caught, as are game fish, and if the management of coarse fish fisheries do not even limit the numbers of fish taken away, then stocks will be depleted. This situation would be exactly the opposite of the over-populated coarse fish fisheries I complain about so bitterly. If this situation of depleted fish stock should come about, then management would have to concentrate their energies on providing safe spawning areas. The protection afforded by these safe spawning areas where fishing is not permitted, is as effective as is the protection afforded by a close season.

8 The Underwater Food Animals

It is an impertinence to give only one chapter to the myriads of 'creepy-crawlies' (as we at Two Lakes call the underwater food animals) when there are so many august authorities who have written so many books about them. Be that as it may, we can only touch upon some of the main points as they affect our subject. Generally speaking, they can make or break any fishery, game or coarse. But before discussing ways of improving the supply of creepy-crawlies, we must understand which fish eats what.

Northern European freshwater fish can be divided roughly into three groups. The most harmless are the vegetable eaters, roach and rudd, for example, which eat quantities of weed. Not that they are entirely vegetarian; on warm summer evenings both these fish can be seen dimpling the surface of the water as they take midges and other flies that float there; they also eat zooplankton. And, we regret to say, at spawning time they eat their own eggs and freshly-hatched fry.

The second category of fish, which eats weed only occasionally, lives on the small underwater creatures of river and lake. These are the carp, the crucian carp, tench, bream, etc., right down the scale to the sticklebacks and minnows. And after these relatively harmless citizens of the underwater world come the highwaymen, the cut-throats, the predators: pike, catfish, zander and perch. A pike of fifteen to twenty kilos in weight can swallow fish of several kilos without any difficulty at all. Catfish, growing to much larger sizes, especially in some of the continental rivers of Europe, are even more aggressive. Both these fish feed on the small underwater creatures only when they are in the fry stage. When they are still only a few centimetres long, they become predators. Perch and zander do not gobble up large fish, but are predators in the sense that they both live on small fish of all species including their own. It follows that they are useful to fishery managers for keeping the coarse fish population down to manageable numbers, eating the small fish but leaving the larger roach, rudd, and bream. Perch and zander will also take the larger creepy-crawlies, such as dragon-fly nymph, and the larvae of the great diving beetle.

Trout and eels have a special place in the feeding habits stakes. Both these fish take small fish, but for some periods they live in the main on the small food animals. When perch lay their eggs in long ribbons on underwater obstacles, some eels gorge themselves on these eggs, while trout can spend many hours of the day, especially in the evenings, feeding on flies drifting on the water surface.

Plankton and Midges

The diet of fish in still water generally includes planktonic crustaceans. The two best known are daphnia and cyclops. Zooplankton, to give them their more common name, are free-floating, and since they cannot withstand a current, they are not usually found in rivers though they can exist in the quiet bays of slow-moving rivers, and indeed I have even found some in an unruffled backwater of the famous River Test. But every healthy lake contains quantities.

Many fish, and nearly all fish in the fry stage, feed on zooplankton, so it stands to reason that we should look for ways of increasing this important food. The first thing that comes to mind is fertilization of a pond or lake. Such a measure can be very beneficial in coarse fish angling waters, although over-fertilization, especially in very hot weather, can lead to pollution and result in heavy losses of fish.

There are several further points I must make on the subject of fertilizer. The water must be neutral. If it is acid, it must be limed sufficiently to bring it at least up to neutral, and only then can you use fertilizer. Moreover lakes and ponds with large reed beds and overgrown with underwater weed should not be treated, as any fertilizer would only encourage their growth. So reeds and weeds must be in correct manageable proportion. And lastly the lake must not have any through-flow when it has been treated, otherwise much of the fertilizer may be washed away.

In coarse fish farming in many Eastern European countries, enormous quantities of plankton are produced in fry ponds by treating the water with 1m³ liquid manure per hectare. For growing-on ponds for older carp, ten times that quantity can be used at different times during the summer. Great care must be taken that the liquid manure is equally distributed along the entire banks of the ponds and it *must* be used at different periods, not all at once, otherwise the larger quantities can cause loss of oxygen. Small doses well distributed over the summer months are safer.

Solid manure from farm animals can be used, too. Small heaps of pig manure should be put in shallow stretches along the banks. It is wise to start with only a short stretch, and after a week or so, to continue with another short stretch. This is safer for beginners, although an experienced manager, who has attended a fishery school and knows the correct proportions, can act more boldly. Some fishermen will object to this method of plankton production. The use of stable manure is quite revolting to their city minds. They would rather not remember that up until quite recently, before the introduction of the artificial fertilizers, our daily bread came from grain grown in fields where the farmers had deposited load upon load of dung from their farm animals. Many older anglers may still remember what wonderful fishing was provided by the village pond or by farm ponds; liquid manure from the farmyards seeped into the ponds and nourished countless food animals for the warm water fish to feed upon. Very large carp and tench, especially, were caught in these ponds.

There are other possibilities of increasing zooplankton. You will remember that freshly flooded land, where the turf has not been removed, produces astonishing results for the first two or three years in the life of a lake. Some recent researches substantiate the claim that the fertility of such newly flooded land will be two or three times that of the lake in later years. All the new reservoirs, in their first years, provide fishermen with some wonderful memories. The angling press publish pictures and stories of monster catches.

Green plants, in their process of decomposition when covered by the advancing waters of the newly created lake, provide ideal conditions for the small animals in the long food chain which ends with the fish, or more accurately, with the fish in our frying pans. We can create similar conditions in small lakes and ponds. The coarse fish farmer on the Continent empties his ponds every year, cultivates them and, after reflooding, the ponds are rejuvenated and once more productive. Of course, lakes and ponds used for angling cannot be emptied every year. But it is possible, in the autumn, to lower the water level to a point which still leaves safe overwintering conditions for the fish. During the winter the frost has helped to break up the exposed mud, and in the early spring, the soil should be cultivated, not too deeply, and very lightly manured. Then a mixture of clover, wheat, oats, lupins, peas and grasses should be sown. When this greenery is nearly half grown, the water level should be raised to flood some part of it. Take great care not to cover too great an expanse of land too soon, or the decomposing plants will cause a loss of oxygen in the water. It is better, really, to seed the lower dry places near the water level much earlier than the areas which will later be covered by the rising waters. These green seeded areas (see Figure 38) must be flooded while the plants

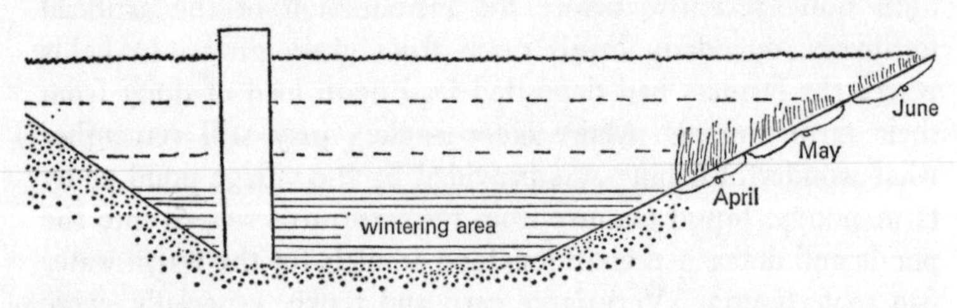

FIGURE 38

are still tender and green; if the flooding is delayed until the plants have matured and become tough, the results will be unsatisfactory.

In lakes where the water level is not controllable, or where no hatches exist or where the water supply is not reliable, you can still farm zooplankton. Fresh green grass, even lawn cuttings, young soft reeds, bulrushes and sedges are all suitable, and can be cut into small pieces and put in heaps into shallow water around the lake side. When decomposition sets in these heaps become rich larders of zooplankton and on some carp ponds in Southern Russia, the plankton has increased up to fifteen times in two or three weeks when this has been done. But for good results the heaps of green-stuff do not have to be in the water. They can be set close to the water's edge, preferably on a sloping bank so that any rain will wash their goodness down into the lake. If possible, mud from the lake, some dung, and some lime should be added to the heaps of green-stuff.

If you want to farm zooplankton in a bigger way, you should dig out one or more shallow ponds, measuring not less than ten by ten metres. The shape is of no consequence, but they should be situated as close to the lake as possible. Ideally, a dam of two or three metres only should separate the lake and the pond. Then it is the same recipe as before: dry out, cultivate, manure lightly and plant, but in this case red clover only should be sown thickly. When the clover is half grown, the pond should be filled with water. It will not be long before the water will be a porridge-like mass of throbbing zooplankton, provided, of course, the weather conditions are normal. The plankton can be scooped out in vast quantities every day, and put into the lake.

On the Continent, chemical fertilizers are used increasingly in this farming but if chemicals are used to fertilize waters, the fishing clubs or private owners who use them must make very certain that they are used correctly. They should contact the manufacturers for explicit instructions where necessary.

These contrived Instant Green Pastures provide ideal living conditions for the larvae of the different midges. While carp, for instance, feed mainly on zooplankton for the first two years of their life, from their third year they feed on midge larvae which they are able to extract from the mud. Autopsies of carp have shown that in some lakes these larvae become the staple diet of older carp.

Day-flies and Sedges

Many fertilizers used in a lake will increase the free-floating vegetable plankton as well as the microscopic plants which grow on the stems and leaves of underwater plants and on submerged timber, stones, etc. These make up part of the diet of the nymphs of the day-flies and many species of snails.

It is well worthwhile, even if only for entertainment, to watch the day-fly nymphs going about their business. You do not need a proper aquarium. Pinch one of your wife's precious pyrex dishes, fill it with lake water and put in the nymphs and some weed. For that matter, put in some snails, and some other sorts of nymphs, and have more to watch. You will see the nymphs grazing on freshly supplied bits of weed, but since the weed never seems to vanish, it is obvious that the creatures have not eaten it. They are working their way up and down and over the weed, nibbling the slimy growth on the plant.

Of the day-flies in lakes the three most important are the sepia dun, which hatches in the spring, the lake olive which hatches in the summer and the pond olive which has the longest hatching season, lasting all through the summer with a few peak periods. Pond olives are quite common in lakes where the temperature seldom rises above 20°C. Of course, this means that the water is also suitable for trout. From the fisherman's point of view it is a useful fly giving sport to nymph and wet-fly fishermen, but good hatches of pond olives give the dry-fly fisherman his chances. These nymphs and others appear in significant numbers in the stomach contents of trout and because the pond olive does even better in a pond or lake where the temperature rises above 20°C, it is valuable as food for coarse fish. Nearly every species of coarse fish, even the predators, eat nymphs in their younger stages.

Should a fishery manager find that the waters in his care are not populated with day-flies, he should make every effort to introduce them, or to reintroduce them if they have been present in the past. It is possible to collect the nymphs from lakes which are rich in them. In early summer, when the water becomes warmer, the nymphs can be caught with a plankton net in the weed close to the bank. We have caught them in great numbers by pulling underwater weed out of the lake, and quickly, before the nymphs have chance to lose their grip on the weed, dropping the lot into a large container of water. Then, handful by handful, we shake the weed and rinse it gently in the water, and most of the nymphs drop out. After all the weed is removed, we strain the water through a plankton net and have a fine catch of thousands of nymphs. If these nymphs are earmarked for restocking, they are put quickly into transporting containers filled three-quarters full with water, and are brought to their new home without delay. Two Lakes has often provided pond olive nymphs for stocking newly created lakes or restocking old ones, and the attempts have been successful, I am glad to say. But always, the numbers have been quite large and great care has been taken in the handling of the creatures. In any transfer of underwater creatures from one water to another it is very important that the temperature range and the chemical character of the lake water stocked are very similar to the old habitat, so we have only supplied lakes much like our own. Great care must also be taken that the temperatures of the transporting water and of the water of the new home are equalized very slowly, the same precaution indeed, that is taken when stocking with fish.

In rivers, too, it is an advantage to stock with fly, if there is not plenty already present. There are some trout farms that collect the eggs of some of the river flies, and will give instructions on how to proceed with the stocking. It is worthwhile to stock with mayfly, particularly. One trout farmer who sells every year a good number of eggs of the various day-flies, has found that many of these stocking attempts ended in failure. If the fly has disappeared from a river, restocking can be successful only when the cause of the disappearance is determined and rectified.

Nearly everything that crawls or swims in the water has some food value though that of sedges and their underwater form, the caddis larvae, must come at the bottom of the scale as their food value is doubtful. Trout may feed on both more than do other fish, but only in exceptional circumstances will the trout make these creatures their staple diet. I have found caddis larvae in carp, tench and bream, and in autopsies I have made on roach I have found that they were full of small caddis larvae with cases made of tiny bits of plant matter. Now, roach eat quite a lot of vegetable matter, so I could not be sure if the roach's objective was the grub itself or its habitation.

You need a sedge population, and certainly trout waters should not be without them. They differ in size, colour and behaviour, and therefore they offer additional variety in fly fishing. Experts identified fifty-six different sedges at Two Lakes, and fly fishing would be the poorer without them. Nevertheless, it is unnecessary to take extra steps to increase the sedge population, because all the general improvements carried out in river or lake benefit the sedges. I have found, however, that if a lake is drained annually, the caddis larvae are killed off in great numbers. Only when there is another sheet of water close by from which egg-laying sedges can venture onto the lake when it is refilled, will there be a new sedge population.

We know that carp, at a certain age, depend to a great extent on the underwater form of midges, and the nymphs of day-flies have considerable food value for many of those species of fish which live generally in mid-water or closer to the surface of the water. Whether it be in running water or in still water, a fishery manager must try to increase any animals which will help make his fish grow and keep them in good condition. Moreover, the less energy that is spent by the fish in gathering food, the greater the growth rate. It is understandable that a fish, in dashing forward to snap up a shrimp, will benefit more from that mouthful than if it has been forced to make many movements in collecting the equivalent weight of the shrimp in a number of tiny animals.

When you read the many learned papers written by experts from many countries about the food value of various sizes of animals, you will find that the results of their investigations and the conclusions that they draw vary a good deal. As you, an ordinary fishery manager, are most likely not a scientist, you have to rely on these scientific papers, and you will balance the various opinions and find a happy medium. You will discover that the bigger the food is in size, the bigger fish it makes. The carp, as we know, is a great feeder on plankton in the first two years of its life; then it progresses to larger and larger morsels of food. Additional to its staple food of the midge larvae, it feeds on the larger aquatic insects, and even tadpoles and newts. Many anglers have discovered that large carp are quite prepared to take small fish and no carp farmer would dare to leave parent carp in a fry pond. A water full of freshwater shrimp, water hog louse, snail, etc. will grow big trout and big coarse fish. Again, the fishery manager has to consider how he can increase the population of these larger food animals.

Water Hog Louse and Shrimp

The easiest to manage is the water hog louse. It has many names which may cause confusion: the water louse, the water hog louse, the hog slater, the pond slater, the pond crawler, and so on. So that there may be no misunderstanding I had better give also its Latin name: *Asellus aquaticus*. This creature looks very like a wood louse – which we can find under almost any bit of rotting wood in our gardens – and is found in lakes and slow running rivers. They are frequently found in rivers such as the Itchen, and in some of the deep slow parts of this river this creature is the staple food of the trout.

The water hog louse has the virtue of being able to live in a great variety of waters; it even manages in water which has become slightly polluted and from which the shrimps, day-flies and sedges have disappeared. It cannot swim and therefore lives on the bottom of the lake or in weed beds and, as a scavenger it performs a useful job as health official or even dustman. I have found dead fish covered with great masses of them. They eat rotting plants. I have kept them in my pyrex dish aquarium and fed them leaves which I have fished out of the lake, and for quite some time, as long as I kept them, they seemed to get along quite happily without dead fish added to their diet. In the slower parts of the chalk streams I have seen them crawling in great numbers amongst star wort and water buttercup, eating the dying leaves. They increase very quickly, so if there is not too large a fish population making their demand for food and yet more food, they can provide a never ending source of food for the fish you want to grow quickly. It is always worth while to introduce more water hog louse to add to the breeding population.

Another important food for our fish is the freshwater shrimp. So long as a river is not polluted and is not too muddy, there will be shrimps in residence. If they find the living conditions to their liking, they will be present in such numbers that the gravel bottom of a stream will look as though it is moving. It is possible to see this phenomenon if the light is right just before darkness falls. Some fishing book authors state that shrimps only live in lakes with a stream flowing through. But though it is true that shrimps are more common in rivers than in lakes, which means that they prefer running water, it is going too far to say that they cannot live without running water. In several parts of Europe I have found shrimps in lakes which had no inflow, and were fed only by the drainage from surrounding land. At Two Lakes, where the feeder stream does not create a through-flow, and actually dries up in summer, there are plenty of shrimps. It has been said, and I would venture to say myself, that lake shrimps tend to be larger than river shrimps. It is reasonable to suggest that you should be careful to stock lakes with shrimps coming from lakes, and rivers with river shrimps.

Fishing book writers also state that shrimps will not survive for more than a few days in an aquarium. However, I have taken shrimps from our lakes and installed a pair of them in that famous pyrex bowl – it is easy to catch a pair because dad swims around carrying mum with him – and have managed to rear several generations of shrimps. I covered the bottom of the dish with sand in which was planted a strand or two of milfoil. I fed the shrimps with decaying beech leaves taken out of the lake, with a few breadcrumbs now and then, and very, very occasionally, as a special treat, with tiny scraps of meat. Over the years I have done this successfully several times.

In the days before pellets became the predominant food for trout in trout farming, some continental trout farmers, especially in Eastern Europe, bred shrimps in great numbers to feed their young trout. They used long ditches, roughly one metre wide and with very little water running through, as their shrimp farms. The shrimp were fed mostly with decaying beech leaves and, once a week, with meat scraps. When they were to be harvested, the leaves were removed and put into a large container with a mesh bottom. As the shrimps worked their way downwards out of the leaves, they fell into another container placed underneath the mesh. It was an easy way to collect them.

If the trout farmers had no shrimp farms they collected shrimps from streams and ditches without much trouble. They rubbed one side of a large jute sack very thoroughly with a meaty bone until tiny bits of meat and blood stuck to it. Then they laid the sack, meaty side down, in a stream, secured the corners with bricks, and left it in position until the next day. Then, with a bucket half full of water near at hand, they quickly lifted the sack into the bucket. From the meaty underside of the sack, the seething mass of shrimps let go their hold and swam into the bucket. If a number of fruity sacks are used, and there are plenty of places where shrimps abound, there can be a good supply of this food for the trout.

Always remember that measures taken to increase the shrimp population increase the water hog louse population as well.

In an angling water, for trout or for coarse fish, these further stratagems can be adapted or adopted. In any feeder stream or ditch in the river system or connected with a lake, a shrimp farm can be started. Some people have found that planting watercress in the shallow bays of a lake or a feeder stream of a river has helped greatly to increase the shrimp population, and when the population became too dense, the overspill migrated into the main river or the lake.

We have tried all these variations at Two Lakes, and with success but we have also found that there are two greedy squads who must be kept away from these food farms, the fish themselves, and the ducks. It is easy to keep the fish out if the shallow bays or the ditches, as the case may be, are netted off with fine mesh plastic. But should ducks, wild or domestic, discover such a rich larder, they become so persistent that in many cases only shooting discourages them. It is too complicated and too expensive to cover an extensive bay or a long ditch with wire, which would be the only way of keeping the ducks out.

Snails

Of all the swimming, floating, crawling, and burrowing creatures the water snails are one of the most important food animals. Because they are slow moving they are easily gathered by the fish and without waste of energy. There are many species of freshwater snails, but a fishery manager, of course, is interested only in those which the fish eat. The way to find out whether a certain species of snail will interest your fish is to take one of the snails between your thumb and forefinger and apply gentle pressure. If the shell cracks easily you can be sure that the fish *will* eat this particular snail. If on the other hand, the shell is so hard that you have to pinch it with force in order to crack it, it is not likely to prove a great favourite.

The two 'bread-and-butter snails' on most fisheries are the wandering snail (*Limnea peregra*) and the great pond snail (*Limnea stagnalis*). Several of the ramshorn snails are also very useful. Indeed, most of these flat coils, to give them their other name, have thin shells and are eaten by many fish. Trout and tench, especially, will pick them up. A fishery manager is wise to keep an eye on the resident snail population and add to it, introducing new species from the streams and lakes in the vicinity.

These local waters are likely to have the same qualities as his own angling waters, so he is relatively sure that his imports will be successful.

There can, however, also be unexpected success with inadvertent imports. One day, in the 1950s, my wife brought home a bunch of watercress from a shop supplied by a local watercress farmer. When she washed the watercress she found quite a number of tiny black snails in the bottom of the bowl. I am no snail expert and thought they were the young of a larger sort of snail. Without more ado I put them into the lake. We never waste any creepy-crawlies that we may find. Then I forgot about them entirely. In the following fishing season, however, one of our fishermen caught a very well-conditioned, seven-pound rainbow trout, on which he decided to perform an autopsy, something he was well able to do being a doctor. Of course, he showed me the result, almost a handful of tiny black snails. Suddenly I remembered the snails from the bunch of watercress, and realized that they were not baby snails, but a new sort I did not know about. I sent a sample of them to a snail expert, and he told me that they were Jenkins' spire shell. Of course, I got busy collecting as much information as I could about this little snail, and came across some very interesting facts.

This little snail used to live in brackish waters in estuaries around the coasts of Britain, Ireland, Holland, Denmark and even along the northern coast of Germany in the Baltic Sea. Then, around 1880, the snail started to wander from its old salty environment into the fresh waters of the rivers. Reports were published in the following twenty to thirty years of the snail being found in some rivers higher and higher upstream. In its journeys it had come up the River Test and reached the watercress farm, but it had never penetrated the side stream up to Two Lakes. In its new habitat this little immigrant indulged in a population explosion. An explanation for this may be that the parasites and other troubles which plagued the little snail in its former environment were unable to survive the change from salt water to fresh water. The snail survived, but not its tormentors.

The number of Jenkins' spire shell varies in the lakes here from year to year. In some years we have them in such numbers that the shallows are black with them, and consequently we introduced a new rule forbidding wading. We did not want the fishermen's big feet squashing such good fish food. In some years they are thin on the ground, and why there should be these variations, I do not know. Be that as it may, our Jenkins' spire shell came to us from Hampshire waters, so we can rate it as local. I have tried to introduce snails of other species from other parts of the country, where soil, water, weed and water temperature were most likely quite different from the conditions at Two Lakes. In general, the various stockings were failures; for instance, I bought a consignment of 50,000 snails from the River Exe, put them into the different lakes, and in the following year not one was to be found.

But once I struck gold. One day as I was walking down a street in Southampton, I saw a sign in the window of a pet shop: 'Snails for Sale.' Of course, I went right in to investigate, and found that the snails were a medium-sized ramshorn. One would make a nice mouthful for a fish. Now, at that time, a fish farm charged between 75p and one pound a thousand for snails, so I thought I would buy a few thousand from the pet shop – probably the entire stock. By great good luck I first asked the price, and I nearly fell over when I was told they were 5p each. I kept a stiff upper lip and bought ten. When I got home I told my wife I had bought 50p's worth of snails, and she wondered where I had put the bucketful. I put the ten snails into the lake and forgot about them, as I had the Jenkins' spire shell, because I was quite sure they would not survive longer than a day or two before the trout had them.

A year later, one of my pumps started to play up, so I put on my rubber boots and climbed into the water to clear off the suction head. I found it covered completely with my ramshorn snails, and when I poked around in the weed I found enormous numbers of them. In the following year they had spread to other parts of Two Lakes, and I would not venture to guess at their numbers. Now, this was a lesson to me because in my wisdom I had always advised those who came to me with their fishery management problems, that they should never bother to stock with less than 10,000 snails if they hoped for a chance of success. Here was an example of ten snails being sufficient. Moreover, the snails had not even come from a water in the near neighbourhood, to the best of my knowledge. It must have been that for these particular snails, the conditions at Two Lakes were ideal.

Crayfish

If a snail makes a good mouthful for a larger fish, a freshwater crayfish can almost be considered a meal. In some trout streams, crayfish are a significant source of food. Many trout fisheries and coarse fish fisheries would dearly love to have them. For many anglers, crayfish in a river mean large fish. Is this true? This is not a question that can be answered with a simple yes or no; there are too many complications. It will not hurt if we go into the matter of what is known about crayfish.

In the business world it is well understood that a middleman in a deal makes the price go up: a product would be cheaper if the producer could sell direct to the consumer. In a manner of speaking the crayfish is a middleman. If there are plenty of snails and shrimps in the water, they become the staple food of the crayfish, but snails and shrimps are the staple food of the fish as well. To what degree is a snail- and shrimp-eating crayfish an improvement, as far as food value is concerned? Up to the present fishery research institutes have not found a satisfactory answer to this question, so a layman must tread very carefully in this area – unlike those anglers who profess to know all the answers. They say that crayfish are scavengers and are not, therefore, in competition with the fish for the same food. While the first point is open to argument, the second is ninety-nine per cent wrong.

Crayfish farmers in Eastern Europe hold that crayfish must be fed on fresh food, and that it is only after a long period of starvation that the creatures will take decaying fish or meat. In fact, crayfish are reported to have starved to death rather than take such food. In many parts of Europe the wild crayfish of streams and lakes are trapped in especially designed traps, which are invariably baited with fresh food.

As well as animal food, they eat vegetable matter. They take the young shoots of underwater weeds and the young shoots and the roots of water plants. For this reason, in captivity, they are fed on cooked carrots and other vegetable roots as well as fresh fish and meat. But in the wild, their diet consists mainly of snails, shrimps, fish eggs, insect larvae, worms, small fish, tadpoles, and anything else they can catch. Unfortunately, they are confirmed cannibals. A large crayfish will attack a smaller one. Even a mother, after her young ones have left her, will eat them, given half a chance.

So these animals have a number of little habits which are not beneficial to a fishery. If, however, you want to stock with them anyway, you must understand something of their needs. Crayfish must have well-oxygenated water to live in. I found that out very quickly in my young days when I put some captured crayfish into a deep aquarium, and they died very quickly. I put the next lot into a large aquarium which had such shallow water that a good proportion of it was in contact with the air. These crayfish lived quite a long time in captivity.

Crayfish must have pure, clean water, and dislike coloured water. They disappear from their haunts if there is the slightest trace of pollution, a trace so minimal that even trout will tolerate it. Pollution is one of the main causes of their dwindling population. Contributory causes are the near-canalization of many streams, which creates straight banks and obliterates hiding-places and, finally, disease. Around 1870 the crayfish population of most European countries was almost entirely destroyed, a disaster similar to the decimation of the British bee by the Isle of Wight disease earlier in this century. To make good this devastating loss other species of crayfish, mostly from the United States of America, were introduced into Europe, and the overseas species became naturalized. A crayfish is a crayfish, so far as the fish are concerned, so there is no nostalgia for the crayfish of yesteryear.

If the water is well oxygenated and pure and uncoloured, you have the basic essentials. You must hope and pray that all will go well and in the meantime get on with making the waters habitable for the creatures. And here you can do a lot. They want hiding-places: roots, holes in the bank and stones, are their natural hiding-places but these may not be plentiful. In that case you can get hold of small earthen drainage pipes, such as farmers use for land drainage, and lay them in good numbers on the stream bed at the rate of about one per square metre. Bundles of brushwood are also very attractive to crayfish, and these can be secured under the bank. If the banks are vertical, try to excavate some holes. We will assume that there is plenty of underwater weed and underwater animal life, because these last are most necessary.

As to the number of crayfish that you should stock, if only one bank of the stream is suitable for the creatures to live in, then not more than 1000 or 1200 crayfish per kilometre should be put in. If both banks are suitable, and the stream is not too small, then 2000 and even up to 3000 can be stocked for each kilometre. A rough guide in a small river or stream is one crayfish per metre of bank.

Some authorities state that crayfish live only in rivers. In point of fact, however, there are many lakes and ponds with a large crayfish population. The best of the still waters for stocking are undoubtedly flooded gravel and clay pits, so long as the summer temperature of the water is not over 25°C; but small, long-established natural ponds have also been successfully stocked, though only when the pond bottoms were not muddy, for crayfish cannot tolerate mud. It follows, therefore, that lakes or ponds in which carp, bream, tench and similar fish thrive, and which generally have muddy bottoms, will not be suitable for crayfish. In short, a lake with well-oxygenated water, a hard bottom and plenty of hiding-places, can be stocked at the rate of about 600 to 800 crayfish per hectare.

These figures have been found satisfactory by fishery managers in Russia and in Germany. The main purpose of the stocking was in order to harvest, later on, a certain percentage of the crayfish population for human consumption. Of course, the fish population was a beneficiary as well. If crayfish, which is actually only a small freshwater lobster, are taken from the water by anglers for eating, then only males should be taken. In stocking, three to four females for each male is about right. Males are much more inclined to cannabilism than are females, so a reduction in their numbers is only to the good. It is easy to distinguish the sexes in several ways, but the surest method is to look at their sex organs. The male has an opening where the last pair of legs are attached to the body, while the female opening is where the third pair of legs joins the body (see Figure 39).

As to the handling of the crayfish, they can be transported in boxes filled with moss. When they arrive in their new home, they must not be put into the water immediately, or you may lose the lot. Keep them in their travelling boxes for twenty to thirty minutes and sprinkle them all the while with water from their new home. The creatures must not then be dumped unceremoniously into the water. Instead, each in turn, must be picked up

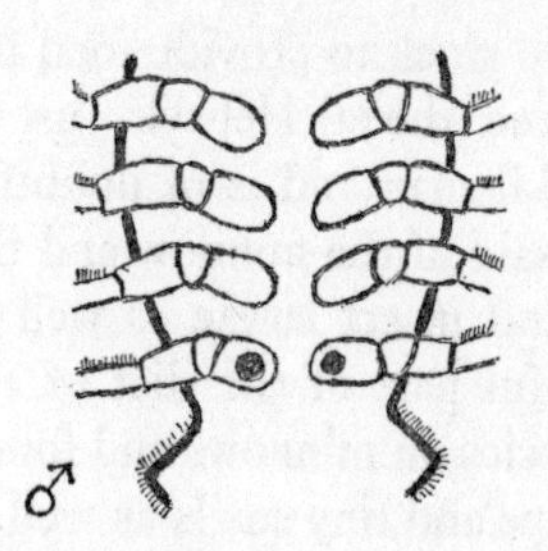

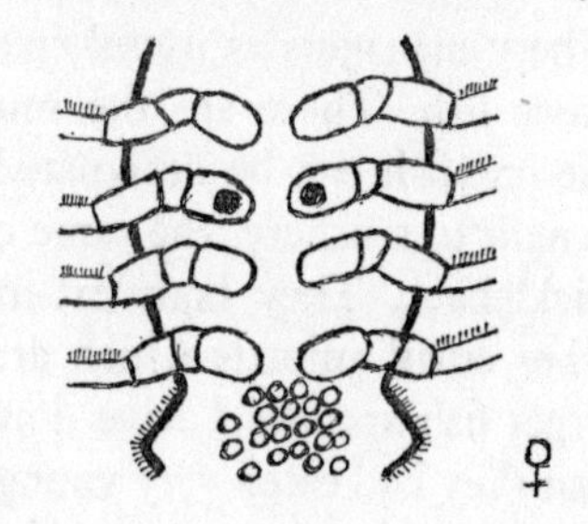

FIGURE 39

just behind its head, turned on its back, and slowly, very slowly put into the water in this position. This enables all the air bubbles in the gills and in the joints to escape, and the crayfish will right itself and crawl away. Another method is to hold the crayfish, again with the tummy upwards, and very slowly put it into the water, shaking it gently underwater, so that the air bubbles can escape. Some people go about things more simply, and are quite content with the results. They pack straw close to the water on the bank and the crayfish are put onto the straw right side up. Instinctively they crawl towards the water, and as they slowly submerge, they themselves press out the dangerous air bubbles. The best time of the year for stocking is in the spring or autumn, not in warm weather.

If possible, there is one fish that must be kept out of any crayfish water, and that is the eel. An eel can follow a crayfish into all its hiding-places and will hunt it assiduously.

Many fishery managers accuse the crayfish of tunnelling under the river banks or the dams of artificial lakes. For what it is worth, my personal opinion is that such long tunnels in the bank are actually dug by water voles, and the crayfish are only availing themselves of suitable accommodation. Holes dug by crayfish are not deep, but just big enough for the animal to be able to push its body in backwards. There the crayfish sit all day with only their antennae sticking out to keep track of what is going on around them. When darkness comes, they leave their hiding-places and go foraging.

Minnow and Stickleback

There are two little fish which strictly speaking do not qualify as 'creepy-crawlies', but none the less are considered by some fishery managers as useful creatures to stock to provide food for other fish. These are the minnow and the stickleback. Just as the crayfish can be designated a middleman and is of doubtful benefit to a fishery, the same can be said of the minnow and the stickleback. They both eat insects and insect larvae as well as other small animals which are a useful part of the diet of the larger fish species. I have done autopsies on minnows and found that they had eaten very young shrimps and tiny snails as well as insects, and, what was particularly interesting, they had eaten the fry of other fish. Admittedly the fry had only just passed the alevin stage, but nevertheless it was surprising to find that such a small fish as a minnow could eat other fish. If you investigate the feeding habits of fish, you find that nearly all species eat their own young and the young of other fish. If the waters suit them, minnows increase at an alarming rate much to the detriment of heavy fly hatches, so welcome in trout fisheries. Consequently, the artificial minnow becomes the best lure in a successful day's trout fishing, and if that is what the members of a club or a private fishery want, then everybody should be happy. There are fisheries, particularly reservoirs, where the minnow and the stickleback are the trout's main food and these fisheries supply fine sport and are very popular. The food-fish relationship is satisfactory in these waters; on the other hand, there are other waters where the introduction of minnows and sticklebacks has done great harm.

A fishery manager should think twice about introducing these small fish. In fishing clubs where the manager is not allowed to make such far-reaching decisions on his own initiative, the decision will be made by the fishery management committee. Should the committee decide to stock with minnows or sticklebacks, and should the fishery manager be against this decision, he would be well advised to insist that the minutes of the meeting be preserved in writing, and the names of the committee members who voted in favour of the decision recorded. Stocking with sticklebacks and minnows has often proved to be a mistake and the likelihood of failure is high. When the fly fishing deteriorates, the anglers will look around for a scapegoat, and who other than the fishery manager will get it in the neck? Should this happen he can turn to the minutes of the fatal committee meeting, and say, 'I told you so!'

above If banks are heavily wooded, fishing piers should be constructed. Here the low water level shows that these piers are built of offcuts of all sorts and covered with grass turf.

right When the water level is at its normal height, the sticks and posts are hidden and the whole pier blends into its surroundings.

left When sexing tench, not only the sexes can be kept separate but also the sizes. Tench have a reputation for hardiness, and there is the temptation to overcrowd the fish in the containers. This must be avoided because injured fish will be attacked by fungus.

below Young men who hope to become fishery managers should be given at the beginning of their training as many dirty, wet, cold, and otherwise uncomfortable jobs as possible, so that they will understand what they are letting themselves in for. Those who are cheerful during and after such jobs are the right men.

The trouble is that once minnows and sticklebacks have established themselves in a fishing water, it is nearly impossible to get rid of them. In lakes that can be drained, or where a fish poison can be used, there is some hope, but in rivers these little fish are there for good. So be warned: before stocking with minnows and sticklebacks, weigh the pros and cons carefully and ask advice from someone with plenty of experience.

I can give you an example of how complicated the question of the food value of a certain fish to another larger fish can become. Several times, research workers have put small fish into test tanks together with young pike, or with perch or trout. The small fish were young carp, bream, rudd, roach and sticklebacks. The predators soon caught and ate all the fish except the sticklebacks; it was only when they became really hungry that they went for the sticklebacks.

The fact remains that all small species of fish which are not of interest from the sporting point of view (not only minnows and sticklebacks, but also loach, gudgeon, bullheads, etc.) compete strongly with the larger species for all available food. Instead of encouraging these little fish, it is wiser to keep their numbers down by trapping, or in special circumstances, by netting.

The most common, and for our purposes, the most useful food animals have been discussed in this chapter. You must not forget that nearly all fish are selective feeders only for short periods; in general they will eat anything that they consider to be edible. But you have only to take a few handfuls of underwater weed, rinse it in a container full of water, and remove the weed, to find an abundance of different creatures. If all these animals were discussed separately, this book would take an unconscionable time to read and who knows how long to research and write! Let us leave it at that.

9 Publicity for Fisheries

This chapter could very well bear the sub-title 'last but not least' for although I have left publicity till the end it is an important subject. Of course, you must wait until your fishery is in being before you start publicizing it. It has happened more than once that reports are published of plans for a new fishery; full details are given, about the number of fishermen, about the catches, and about how lucky the fishing world is that there will be a fishery of such outstanding excellence, and then nothing more is heard, ever again. The fishing world is either contemptuous or bored by such non-events. The more sensible move, therefore, is to get everything ready and then, instead of telling people how good it is, telling them to come and try it.

Advertisements for rods are the first step in your publicity campaign, and you should be careful to avoid the initial mistake of wording your advertisement badly. You could harm your fishery before you even start in business. I could give you countless examples of bad advertisements, but we will take the positive approach and give an example of a really good effort:

RIVER TROUT FISHING
season ticket only, one day per week,
five fish bag limit, average weight 1 kg. Price £120.
Write to: Water Meadow Estate Office, Hampshire.

All the information is there, so much correspondence is saved. As it is a river fishery, a still water fisherman will not apply. It is a season ticket water, so it is pointless for anybody to try for a day ticket. The bag limit and the average weight are stated, the price is stated, and this gives an idea of what can be expected. Lastly, the full name and address of the estate are given, so an applicant knows where it is, which is an important point when travelling must be a consideration.

Here are examples of bad advertisements:

FIRST CLASS TROUT FISHING
in our trout lake for £3 a season . . .

'First class' should come out. Three pounds a season is a laughably small sum, and trout fishing at this price could never be first class. But it is possible that somebody may want to take on a rod in the hope that maybe the fishery was stocked initially with, say, a hundred thousand fry which had been left to grow on. Or perhaps somebody may hope that the fishing is completely wild.

TROUT FISHING
a few full and half rods to let for the coming season. . . .

This advertisement appeared in the late summer, and continued all through the autumn and winter months, right into the next season. The mistake here is the phrase 'a few'. I looked it up in the dictionary, out of curiosity, and the definition is 'small in number . . . not many', but no exact number is given. I asked my fishermen how they would interpret 'a few', and they suggested three, four, five and one of them suggested six. Nobody suggested seven or more. When it first appeared, this advertisement gave everybody to understand that there were up to six vacancies in this fishery. All well and good. But if the advertisement appears week after week and month after month still offering a few rods, everybody knows that only six rods were required but they have not been let and everybody wonders why. Alternatively, if the advertisement is run for only one to three weeks, 'a few' could be used. The advertiser gives the impression that there are not many opportunities available for fishermen, so they had better hurry and 'get in first'. I am always very dubious about any advertisement which is couched in now-or-never terms and I would wager that most fishermen would feel the same.

Here is yet another ill-considered advertisement:

TROUT FISHING a one day a week rod for £25.
Payment in three instalments. . . .

If the rod is £25 for one day a week throughout the season, it is too cheap. If the price is £25 for each day, it is too expensive. As for payment by instalment, that is asking for trouble.

Sometimes there are advertisements which make or imply criticisms of other fisheries. This is a really stupid way of going about things as any fisherman reading the advertisement will see and dislike the spite and envy that prompted the wording. Fishermen aren't stupid.

To sum up, avoid words and phrases which can give the wrong impression. Avoid the word 'exclusive'. Try to be as informative as possible in the fewest possible words. Do not be unkind about the competition.

I have found that the best method is to place the same ad two weeks running in a fishing publication in the autumn after the season finishes, and if there is not sufficient response, then do the same thing for two weeks before the next season commences. You can advertise in two or three fishing publications simultaneously. You may still not find the number of rods you want, but don't panic. Try to be satisfied with what you have and don't start imploring people to come. You would place yourself at a disadvantage that would take quite some years to counteract. Besides, you cannot force people to come and fish if they don't want to! If you provide fishing which is good value for money you will find that each new season brings more enquiries, until eventually you don't need to advertise at all.

Nevertheless, even a long-established fishery which is fully booked should put an ad in the angling press every two or three years. Nobody should be so conceited as to think that everybody has heard of his fishery, and besides you can inform those people who reckon that it would be hopeless to try for a rod, that they can go on the waiting list at least. Furthermore, if, in spite of being very much in demand, and in spite of being fully booked, you *do* advertise, you undermine the confidence of your rogue rods, and the fear of replacement will help them to remember their manners!

It is just as well, before we leave the subject, to remind you that *where* you place your advertisement is important. Do not advertise in, say, a publication for motor cycle enthusiasts, or gardening devotees, or in a caterers' journal. If you have a game fishery, select those publications which are specifically for game fish, although any fishing paper will be fruitful.

Once you have got your rods, you want to keep them. There are quite a number of clubs and fisheries that have to exert themselves to find another lot of new rods each season, while other fisheries seldom let out even so much as a murmur of publicity, because their fishermen remain year after year, and rods becoming vacant are 'self-letting' so to speak. I sincerely hope you will not be one of the former clubs or fisheries, while as to the latter, in spite of their security, it cannot hurt them to keep in the public eye. Publicity, however, should be discreet, rather like a gentle cough to remind everybody of your presence. The essence of such refined publicity is to be mentioned in fishing books. An angling writer wants to give information which is interesting and authentic. He must do so, otherwise he will not have anything to write about. If a writer fishes with you and finds something of note and writes about it, it can only do you good. Over the years Two Lakes has had several well-known writers as season rods, and quite a number of books have been published in which Two Lakes is described and discussed at length. It all helps the reputation of a fishery, and as a fringe benefit it gives pleasure to the rods. Books are the most permanent form of publicity. People lend them to their friends and when they are eventually resold they usually end in a second-hand book shop from which they are bought to be read yet again.

Articles in the angling press or, though this will occur less often, in the national press, are of value, so long as they are not melodramatic. If you yourself have a bent for writing, you can produce an article on some interesting topic and send it in to a paper. You also can and should send brief notes to the angling press if you have something important to report.

Your fishing reports during the season are valuable publicity. Make them factual (never wander from the truth) and where you mention names, be sure that you have the initials and the spelling right. Post them off well before the date of publication, and if possible have them typed in double spacing, with wide margins. Try to save the editor as much trouble as possible. When you send in your end of season report, remember that your average weight is an important item of news. Some fisheries fiddle their average weight, and the only persons who are taken in by the fiddle are the perpetrator and his accomplices. No one else is. When the fishermen have caught fish of half a kilo or a little over, how can you convince them that the average weight works out at a kilo? Publish the true average weight of all the fish included in the total bag for the season.

Even when you report the average weight honestly, you may find your truthfulness questioned by anglers who have had a bad season. At Two Lakes I use the following stratagem to settle this question once and for all. Every year, towards the end of the season, I approach my fishermen as they sit in groups, eating their sandwiches, and I ask those who I know keep careful records, I ask in a loud voice, how many trout they have caught and what is their average weight. One may say his average is over a kilo, another that his is one kilo, and yet another that his average is a little below the kilo mark. So the ball starts to roll, and they are soon discussing the subject and comparing notes. I do this each day of the week and as several of my rods fish two days a week they meet with more than one group. Within a week all the rods fishing at Two Lakes have a rough idea of average weights achieved, and when I work out the average weight for the whole fishery, they realize I am telling the truth. My fishermen meet others from different waters and the news spreads. Particularly in club fisheries, all figures must be absolutely accurate and beyond dispute, otherwise the publicity of the fishing reports will work against the fishery.

While we are on the subject of the angling press, give a thought to the photographs you will send in for publication. First of all, put yourself in the editor's shoes. On his desk there are a number of photographs. With such a selection it is understandable that he will pick out those which are a little unusual. Moreover, if the photograph is not only out of the ordinary but is also sharp, well balanced, glossy, *and has a caption on the back*, he is quite likely to pounce on it. Remember the editor wants good photographs. There are too many pictures which portray an angler grinning from ear to ear and holding up a very dead fish. Try to be different and try to be better.

When you are having the photograph taken, remember that the fish is what matters. The background, the fisherman and how he is holding the fish are side issues. For instance, a three-kilo trout looks much more impressive when it is held by your small daughter than by yourself, although your name can still be mentioned in the caption. It is eye-catching if you have your dog sitting beside your big salmon. There are many fishermens' faces published in an angling paper, but not many dog's faces. Or, if it comes to it, let your cat sit beside your big catch, if, of course, you can prevent the cat from eating it.

Photographs of coarse fish, when it is intended to return the fish alive to the water after the picture-taking, are more difficult. The fish must be handled carefully and as little as possible, so it is best to photograph them as they lie on the ground. Most anglers will then kneel behind their catch.

Of course, it is understandable that many anglers who have never had their pictures published will seize the opportunity to have their faces in the papers, but, notwithstanding, a little imagination should be used in the presentation. Photographs are cost-free publicity, and indeed most newspapers will even pay for a picture if it is published.

A club or fishery need not confine themselves to sending only photographs of fish to the papers. Improvements or alterations may be worth photographing and reporting. For instance, my Alsatian dogs, over the years, have caught quite a good bag of poachers. Should they catch one again (they leave us pretty well alone now!) we will send the dog's picture to the angling press. The picture will be a close-up to show its impressive jaws and the score of the catch will be reported. Naturally we will mention that Two Lakes is where fishermen catch lots of trout, and big ones, as well as where Alsatians catch poachers.

There is one sort of publicity that can be very damaging, whatever the state of your fishery, fully booked or not fully booked, and that is pre-season publicity, in which you inform everyone of what they will catch in the coming season. You may have ordered all your trout. You may even have them in your stews. But something may happen to the trout farm which makes delivery impossible or the fish in the stew ponds may suffer some sort of disaster or they could even be stolen. You are forced to make do with fewer and probably smaller fish, if you have been able to find replacements at all. Trout farms cannot supply fish at a moment's notice. Now, your pre-season publicity has put it about that fishermen will catch fish of one kilo and they have come from far and wide to do just this. They are going to be very sour when their expectations are not fulfilled and you will be branded a liar. However innocent you may be of deliberate misrepresentation, you will still be branded as a liar, and nobody will ever forget it.

Then there is television, still another medium for publicity. At Two Lakes we have had various television personalities making fishing programmes, and all has gone well, because they were anglers and knew what they were talking about. But making a television programme to boost your fishery is not easy. If you do not know those involved in making the film well, you will have very little influence. Sometimes these people are not anglers themselves and the film that they make may be good entertainment but could give a wrong and harmful impression of your fishery. Fishermen will be put off if the fishery is made to resemble a seaside resort. Day ticket waters will gain most benefit from a television programme, and the more fish that are filmed being caught, the better. This will bring fishermen flocking in. If you do have a television programme made about your fishery, have it clearly understood that the name of the fishery is to be mentioned.

It may appear from what I have said so far that I am referring only to game fisheries, which is not so. Advertising and publicity for coarse fish fisheries are basically the same as for game fisheries, the only shade of difference being that in advertisements for coarse fish fisheries more details must be given.

The best publicity you can ever hope to have for your fishery is that which comes from the jungle drums or the grapevine: reputation. Never forget that it takes quite a time to build up a reputation of giving value for money and being completely trustworthy. This reputation must be guarded fiercely by continuing to give value for money, even when giving the value may eat somewhat into your profit, and by continuing to be absolutely straight in all your dealings. You must be prepared to find that, parallel with your good reputation, will run the criticism of your detractors: the better your reputation, the more unkind this will be. Never take this to heart and never attempt to answer your critics, because you will find yourself involved in an endless and profitless wrangle. Of course, there is always the possibility that the criticisms are constructive, in which case you incorporate them promptly into your working plans.

Publicity is a powerful tool. Handled correctly it can be of great benefit to your fishery, while handled badly it can do harm which will take years to undo. Your best publicity is truth told in such a way that it catches the attention of those people you want to fish your waters.

And so we come to the end. In this book I have tried to give accurate information, and as much information as space permits, drawing always on my own experience. My sincere hope is that it will be a useful guide to managers and anglers too. After twenty-eight years of running a successful fishery I have not lost any of my enthusiasm for this as a way of life. I hope others may enjoy it equally.

Index

Abstraction, 95
Additional growth (carp), 170, 171
(trout), 137, 138
Advertisements, 84, 97, 138, 194–196
Alsatian dogs, 91, 117, 135
Angling clubs, 13, 42, 64, 166, 167, 169, 192, 199
Average weight, 198

Backflow, 20, 50
Bag limit, 61
Barbel, 160
Beats, 96
Boats, 89, 139
Bream, 52, 154–163, 165, 167, 174, 175, 176, 181, 193
Brown trout, 111, 112, 122, 133–136, 147
Bulldozer, 36–46
Bullhead, 193

Caddis, 24, 81, 181
Carp, 11, 14, 72, 108, 129, 146, 154–163, 164, 171, 174, 175, 177, 179, 181, 182, 193
Catfish, 174, 175
Chain scythe, 107
Chalk, 33, 43
Chalk stream, 15, 68, 77, 82, 96, 132, 176, 183
Chemical weed killers, 124
Chub, 147–149
Close season, 62, 173
Contractors, 36, 38
Cork hatch, 25–28
Cormorant, 143
Crayfish, 188–191
Crucian carp, 147, 163–167, 175

Dam, 36–59
Day flies, 175, 179–182, 183, 192
Day tickets, 70, 92
Disease, 149, 158, 163, 172, 189
Dogs, 90, 91, 117, 118, 199
Dragline, 36, 103, 110
Drainage, 22–25, 45, 47, 56, 95, 110, 123
Dry fly/wet fly controversy, 67, 77, 180

Eel, 118, 147–149, 158, 171, 176, 191
Electrical fishing, 145
Elver trap, 51, 56
Estimates (for lake building), 36–38
Evaporation, 17, 73
Experts and consultants, 11

Feeders, 116
Femel system, 26
Fertilizers, 176–179
Finance, 95–101
Fish barrier, 49
Fish box trap, 52–55
Fish farming, 9, 10, 11, 14, 24, 27, 54, 60, 64, 108, 114, 116, 138–139, 155–156, 178, 184, 199
Fishing licences, 66, 67
Fishing piers, 139–141
Fishing reports, 197–198
Fishing time, 92
Fry (*see* Stocking)

General licence, 66, 67
Grass carp, 128–130
Gravel pits, 12, 16, 146
Grebe, 143
Guests, 82–88
Gudgeon, 193
Gulls, 121

Hatchery, 113
Herons, 119–121, 146

Ice, 141
Inflow, 17, 47, 56, 115
Insurance, 72

Keepers, 96–99, 117, 145
Kingfisher, 121, 146

Lakes, 12, 56, 170–171, 174, 179, 180, 184
Landscaping, 56, 57–59
Leather carp, 160, 161
Loach, 193
Log book, 73–79

Mayfly, 181
Manure, 177–179
Midges, 175–179, 182
Mink, 118, 119, 143
Minnow, 191–193
Monk, (sluice), 22–35, 38, 45, 47, 50, 52, 73, 115, 123, 141, 144
Mud, 24, 46, 52, 53, 108–110, 131, 139, 141, 154, 157, 178, 183, 190
Mud pan, 109–110
Mud pumps, 110

Nets, 152, 161, 173
Netting, 145, 152, 165, 166, 169, 171
Nymphs, 16, 24, 144, 180

Otter, 118, 143
Overflow, 16, 20–21, 26, 34, 45–50, 55, 56, 73, 115
Oxygen, 106, 115, 122, 123, 127, 141, 178, 189, 190

pH value, 16, 176
Payment for tickets, 63–66
Pellets, 115, 132
Perch, 129, 143, 147, 149–154, 158, 163, 167, 171, 172, 175, 176
Photographs, 198, 199
Pike, 143, 144–147, 157, 161, 164, 166, 173, 175
Planning permission, 18, 20
Plankton, 16, 24, 149, 153, 165, 166, 175, 176–179, 180, 182
Poachers, 80, 114, 116
Poison, 142, 193
Pollution, 9, 16, 95, 163, 176, 183, 189
Polythene sheets, 17, 125–127
Predators, 161, 165, 175, 176
Pressure mats, 118
Pre-season publicity, 199
Publicity, 194–201
Put and take, 12, 139, 160
Pumping, 16

Raft, 124, 125
Rainbow trout, 90, 111, 122, 133, 134–139, 147, 165, 186
Reeds and rushes, 156, 169, 176
Reputation, 200
Reservoirs, 42, 70, 77, 89, 92, 122
Returning fish, 78–82, 143
Roach, 52, 147, 158, 160, 161, 163–167, 171, 175–176, 181, 193
Rod letting, 12, 63
Rod sharing, 82–85
Rudd, 147, 160, 163–167, 175–176, 193
Rules, 60–94

Scale reading, 158, 172
Scraper, 36
Season tickets, 70
Sedges, 179–181, 183
Seepage, 18, 21, 42, 43, 48
Sexing tench, 168
Shrimp, 24, 81, 104, 105, 128, 129, 132, 144, 149, 182–185, 188, 192
Shrubs, 21, 39, 59
Silt, 21
Site, 13–19
Size limit, 173, 174
Snails, 24, 81, 105, 128–129, 144, 179–180, 185–188, 192
    Great pond snail, 185
    Jenkins spire shell, 90
    Ramshorn snail, 185
    Wandering snail, 185
Soil, 42, 43, 48
Stew pond, 24, 34, 39, 113–116, 132, 199
Stickleback, 191–193
Stocking, 74, 77, 80, 93, 96–99, 101, 110–113, 117, 131–139, 146, 148, 154, 157, 160, 172–174, 190–192
Stream alterations, 101
Surface feeding, 132
Syndicates, 12–13

Television, 200
Temperature, 17, 122, 155, 172, 180, 181, 187, 190
Tench, 11, 52, 54, 90, 129, 144, 146, 158, 164, 167–173, 175, 177, 181
Transport, 172
Traps, 52–54, 119, 145, 165, 193
Trees, 21, 27, 39, 56–59, 139